SCIENCE

CurriculumBank

KEY STAGE TWO
SCOTTISH LEVELS C

MATERIALS AND
THEIR PROPERTIES

Published by Scholastic Ltd,
Villiers House,
Clarendon Avenue,
Leamington Spa,
Warwickshire CV32 5PR
Text © 1995 Suzanne Kirk
© 1995 Scholastic Limited

8 9 0   0 1 2 3 4 5

AUTHOR
SUZANNE KIRK

EDITORS
NOEL PRITCHARD AND JOEL LANE

ASSISTANT EDITOR
LIBBY WEAVER

SERIES DESIGNER
LYNNE JOESBURY

DESIGNER
CLARE BREWER

ILLUSTRATIONS
RHIAN NEST JAMES

COVER ILLUSTRATION
JONATHAN BENTLEY

INFORMATION TECHNOLOGY
MARTIN BLOWS

SCOTTISH 5–14 LINKS
MARGARET SCOTT AND SUSAN GOW

Designed using Aldus Pagemaker

British Library Cataloguing-in-Publication Data
A catalogue record for this book is available from the
British Library.

ISBN 0-590-53395-9

Contents

INTRODUCTION   5

Overview grid   9

CLASSIFYING MATERIALS   13

CHANGING MATERIALS   53

SEPARATING MIXTURES   77

INVESTIGATIONS   87

ASSESSMENT   97

PHOTOCOPIABLES   101

IT links   158

Cross-curricular links   160

Introduction

Scholastic Curriculum Bank is a series for all primary teachers, providing an essential planning tool for devising comprehensive schemes of work as well as an easily accessible and varied bank of practical, classroom-tested activities with photocopiable resources.

Designed to help planning for and implementation of progression, differentiation and assessment, *Scholastic Curriculum Bank* offers a structured range of stimulating activities with clearly-stated learning objectives that reflect the programmes of study, and detailed lesson plans that allow busy teachers to put ideas into practice with the minimum amount of preparation time. The photocopiable sheets that accompany many of the activities provide ways of integrating purposeful application of knowledge and skills, differentiation, assessment and record-keeping.

Opportunities for formative assessment are highlighted where appropriate within the activities, while separate summative assessment activities give guidelines for analysis and subsequent action. Ways of using information technology for different purposes and within different contexts, as a tool for communicating and handling information and as a method for investigating, are integrated into the activities where appropriate, and more explicit guidance is provided at the end of the book.

The series covers all the primary curriculum subjects with separate books for Key Stages 1 and 2 or Scottish Levels A–B and C–E. It can be used as a flexible resource with any scheme, to fulfil National Curriculum and Scottish 5–14 requirements and to provide children with a variety of different learning experiences that will lead to effective acquisition of skills and knowledge.

MATERIALS

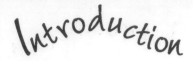

SCHOLASTIC CURRICULUM BANK SCIENCE

The *Scholastic Curriculum Bank Science* books enable teachers to plan comprehensive and structured coverage of the primary science curriculum and pupils to develop the required skills, knowledge and understanding through activities that promote scientific thinking and ways of working.

Each book covers one key stage. At Key Stage 1/Scottish levels A–B, all areas of science are covered in one book. At Key Stage 2, there are three books which reflect the sections of the programme of study (Life Processes and Living Things, Materials and their Properties and Physical Processes). Experimental and Investigative science is integrated into the three Key Stage 2/Scottish levels C–E books, so that it is tackled in context.

Bank of activities

This book provides a bank of activities that can be used in many different ways – to form a framework for a scheme of work; to add breadth and variety to an existing scheme; or to supplement a particular topic. The activities are designed to address a number of important areas of study.

Systematic enquiry

A wide range of activities has been presented, to create opportunities for focused exploration and investigation to acquire scientific knowledge, understanding and skills. The activities involve both firsthand experience and the use of other sources of information. Opportunities for the use of IT for storing, retrieving and presenting information, and for investigative purposes, are suggested throughout.

Communication skills

The activities aim to develop children's communication skills by encouraging them to:
▲ ask questions;
▲ learn and use scientific vocabulary;
▲ use standard measures;
▲ discuss findings with others;
▲ present data in a variety of different ways.

Science in everyday life

Through a variety of domestic and environmental contexts, pupils are able to acquire an awareness of the importance of science in everyday life, of the part science has played in the development of many of the things they use, and of the need to treat their environment with care and sensitivity.

The nature of scientific ideas

The activities will help children to understand that scientific knowledge and understanding rely on evidence, and that scientific evidence can be obtained in a number of ways.

They will also help children to realise that science can provide explanations for many of the things that happen around them.

Health and safety

The activities encourage children to develop their knowledge and understanding of health and safety when working with living things and with materials. They will help pupils to recognise potential hazards to themselves and others, assess the risks to themselves and others, and take action to help control the risks.

Lesson plans

Detailed lesson plans, under clear headings, are given for each activity and provide material for immediate implementation in the classroom. The structure for each activity is as follows:

Activity title box

The information contained in the box at the beginning of each activity outlines the following key aspects:
▲ *Activity title and learning objective* – For each activity, a clearly-stated learning objective is given in bold italics. These learning objectives break down aspects of the programmes of study into manageable, hierarchical teaching and learning chunks, and their purpose is to aid planning for progression. These objectives can be easily referenced to the National Curriculum and Scottish 5–14 requirements by using the overview grids at the end of this chapter (pages 9 to 12).
▲ *Class organisation/Likely duration* – Icons ♰♰ and ◷ signpost the suggested group sizes for each activity and the approximate amount of time required to complete it.
▲ *Safety* – Where necessary, safety considerations are flagged with the ⚠ icon.

MATERIALS

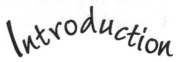

Introduction

Previous skills/knowledge needed
Information is given here when it is necessary for the children to have acquired specific knowledge or skills prior to carrying out the activity.

Key background information
The information in this section is intended to help the teacher to understand the scientific concepts and ideas covered in each activity. It generally goes beyond the level of understanding expected of most children, but will help to give the teacher confidence to ask and answer questions and to guide the children in their investigations.

Preparation
Advice is given for those occasions where it is necessary for the teacher to prime the pupils for the activity or to prepare materials, or to set up a display or activity ahead of time.

Resources needed
All of the materials needed to carry out the activity are listed, so that either the pupils or the teacher can gather them together easily before the beginning of the teaching session.

What to do
Easy-to-follow, step-by-step instructions are given for carrying out the activity, including (where appropriate) suggested questions for the teacher to ask the pupils to help instigate discussion and stimulate investigation.

Suggestion(s) for extension/support
Ideas are given for ways of providing for easy differentiation where activities lend themselves to this purpose. In all cases, suggestions are provided as to how each activity can be modified for the less able or extended for the more able.

Assessment opportunities
Where appropriate, opportunities for formative assessment of the children's work during or after a specific activity are highlighted.

Opportunities for IT
Where opportunities for IT present themselves, these are briefly outlined with reference to particularly suitable types of program. The chart on page 159 presents specific areas of IT covered in the activities, together with more detailed support on how to apply particular types of program. Selected lesson plans serve as models for other activities by providing more comprehensive guidance on the application of IT, and these are indicated by the bold page numbers on the grid and the 🖳 icon at the start of an activity.

Display ideas
Where they are relevant and innovative, display ideas are incorporated into activity plans and illustrated with examples.

Other aspects of the Science PoS covered
Inevitably, activities will cover aspects of the programmes of study in other areas of the science curriculum; and in particular, Experimental and Investigative Science will be a feature of many of them. These links are highlighted under this heading.

Reference to photocopiable sheets
Where activities include photocopiable activity sheets, small reproductions of these are included in the lesson plans, together with guidance notes for their use and, where appropriate, suggested answers.

Investigations
Although aspects of Experimental and Investigative Science will be integral to most activities, each book includes a separate section of investigations and real-life problem-solving activities. These activities are more open-ended than

MATERIALS

The properties of materials, the uses we make of them and the processes in which materials are involved have a direct influence on our lives. We do not always appreciate how our everyday activities are determined by the materials available to us and the uses we make of them. This book aims to raise children's awareness of the relevance of familiar materials to their lives; it will show them that almost everything they do, whether getting dressed, sitting on a chair, using a knife and fork, riding in a car or sleeping in a bed, is dependent on the properties of the materials involved.

Early human societies relied on bone, wood, clay and rock for tools and building. Later, the strength and durability of metals was exploited, then with rapid advances in technology, plastic and other synthetic materials of great versatility were developed.

Children will come to appreciate how we choose materials to suit our needs: rubber for its flexibility; wood for its thermal qualities and because it is attractive and easy to work with; and plastic because it is lightweight and can be produced in many different forms. Some materials are altered only slightly before use; others undergo complex chemical changes before we are satisfied with their properties.

Increasingly, materials are discarded after we have finished with them; their disposal causes problems, whether they are buried, burned or dumped at sea. The once useful properties of durability, hardness and strength prove a disadvantage in this context. To avoid further waste of materials, recycling initiatives have been developed and ways of making more use of sustainable resources are being promoted. As the children discuss, ask questions, predict, make comparisons and draw conclusions, they will begin to understand the value of certain materials to our confirmed lifestyle and see that the way we live today is greatly influenced by our dependence on the use of wood, metal and plastic.

The processes of heating, cooling, freezing, melting, evaporating, condensing, mixing and dissolving are happening all around us. Activities in this book will increase children's awareness of the effects these processes have on our lives, and how we adopt them to suit our needs. Where materials have been mixed together, children are shown how we need to use the processes of sieving, filtering and evaporating as methods of separation.

The study of materials and their properties provides a wealth of opportunities for children to understand more about the world in which they live. This book helps children to develop their understanding and awareness of science, using their skills of observation and investigation and recording their ideas, plans and conclusions.

those elsewhere in the book, and provide opportunities to test ideas and carry out whole investigations, utilising and building on content knowledge. Guidance for the teacher on concepts likely to emerge from such investigations is given. Activities suitable for investigations are flagged by the ⚘ icon.

Assessment

This chapter provides a range of tasks related to the main areas of study covered elsewhere in the book that can be used for summative assessment purposes. The activities have been designed so that they can either be used as individual tasks to provide the teacher with an ongoing evaluation of the children's progress or, alternatively, be presented together as a form of summative assessment at the end of a whole unit or at the end of Key Stage 2. The worksheets that make up the tasks can be found at the end of the Photocopiable section (pages 146 to 157). Activities intended for assessment purposes are flagged by the ✎ icon.

Photocopiable activity sheets

Many of the activities are accompanied by photocopiable activity sheets. There may be more than one version of some activities; or an activity sheet may be 'generic', with a facility for the teacher to fill in the appropriate task in order to provide differentiation by task. Other sheets may be more open-ended, to provide differentiation by outcome.

Cross-curricular links

Cross-curricular links are identified on a simple grid which cross-references the particular areas of study in science to the programmes of study for other subjects in the curriculum, and where appropriate provides suggestions for activities. (See page 160.)

MATERIALS

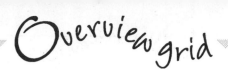

Learning objective	PoS/AO	Content	Type of activity	Page
Classifying materials				
A wide variety of materials exists.	1a. *Materials from Earth: Level B.*	Examining and sorting common objects a) using any criteria, b) according to material.	Group discussion. Sorting and presenting to rest of class. Photocopiable pages (PCPs) for recording. Collecting.	14
Materials have different properties.	1a. *As above: Level B.*	Examining objects of same material. Looking for similarities and differences.	Group investigation. Class discussion. PCP for recording.	16
Some materials are harder than others.	1a. *As above: Level B.*	Testing common materials for hardness. Making comparisons.	Class discussion. Pairs or small-group investigation. PCPs to record planning and results.	17
Some materials are stronger than others.	1a. *As above: Level B.*	Testing types of paper for strength. Comparing strengths.	Class discussion. Pairs investigating and reporting back to class. PCPs for recording.	19
Some materials are more flexible than others.	*1a.* *As above: Level B.*	Collecting flexible items. Testing and examining flexible materials.	Class discussion. Pairs or small groups testing. PCP for recording.	21
Some materials float in water, others sink.	1a. *As above: Level C.*	Testing materials for buoyancy.	Class or group investigation. PCP for recording.	22
Some materials soak up water more than others.	1a. *As above: Level B.*	Testing fabrics to compare their water-absorbing properties.	Class introduction. Pairs investigating. Class discussion. PCP for recording.	23
Some materials respond to magnetic forces.	1a. *Forces and their Effects: Level B.*	Testing a range of materials with a magnet.	Pairs testing and comparing. PCP for recording.	25
Heat travels from a warmer to a cooler material.	1b. *Properties and Uses of Energy: Level B.*	Exploring the conduction of heat.	Class discussion and investigation. PCP for recording.	26
Some materials conduct heat more effectively than others.	1b. *As above: Level C.*	Investigating conduction in a range of materials.	Class discussion. Group or class investigation.	27
Materials which are bad conductors of heat are good insulators of heat.	1b. *As above: Level C.*	Testing building materials for their insulation properties.	Class discussion. Group or class investigation. PCP for recording.	29
Materials which are good thermal insulators are useful for keeping things warm.	1b. *As above: Level C.*	Survey of school to detect heat escaping.	Class discussion. Pairs, group or class survey.	30
Materials which are thermal insulators are useful at home.	1b. *As above: Level C.*	Discussing and collecting examples of thermal insulation in the kitchen.	Class discussion. Individual recording. PCP.	32

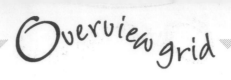

Learning objective	PoS/AO	Content	Type of activity	Page
Clothing is important in keeping us warm and is often designed to take advantage of the insulation properties of air.	1b. *As above: Level B.*	Examining fabrics. Comparing their insulating properties.	Class discussion. Individuals or pairs. PCP.	33
Some materials are better at conducting electricity than others.	1c. *As above: Level C.*	Testing materials for their electrical conductivity.	Class introduction. Pairs or small groups testing. PCP for recording.	34
Natural materials can be changed for people to use.	1a. *Materials from Earth: Level B.*	Discussion; examining raw materials, looking at changes made by humans.	Class discussion. Individual recording. Group discussion.	35
The properties of a material determine its use.	1a. *As above: Level B.*	Examining everyday items; deciding why they were made of certain materials.	Class discussion. Individual or paired working. PCPs for recording.	37
Types of rocks are different from each other in their appearance and texture.	1d. *As above: Level B.*	Examining rock samples; making comparisons.	Class discussion. Pairs investigating. PCPs for recording.	38
Some rocks are harder than others.	1d. *As above: Level B.*	Testing rocks for hardness.	Class discussion. Paired testing.	39
Water can pass through some rocks.	1d. *As above: Level C.*	Testing rock samples and their reactions to water.	Class discussion and planning. Paired testing.	40
Soils are different from each other in their appearance and texture.	1d. *As above: Level C.*	Examining soil samples. Making comparisons.	Pairs discussing and investigating. PCPs for recording.	41
Water passes through soils at different rates.	1d. *As above: Level D.*	Planning and observing water passing through different soil samples.	Small groups.	42
Materials can be grouped into solids, liquids and gases.	1e. *As above: Level C.*	Identifying and listing solids, liquids and gases.	Class discussion. Paired discussion. PCP.	44
Liquids find their own level and take the shape of whatever container they are in.	1e. *As above: Level B.*	Observing liquids in a variety of containers.	Class or group demonstration.	45
Unlike solids and gases, liquids fall in drops.	1e. *As above: Level C.*	Exploring the formation of drops by different liquids.	Paired discussion.	46
Gases spread and fill spaces, therefore they are difficult to control.	1e. *As above: Level B.*	Collecting evidence of gases. Looking for ways of containing gases.	Class demonstration and discussion. Individual recording.	47
As temperature increases, air expands and rises.	1e. *As above: Level B.*	Looking for evidence of air expanding and rising. Making air current detectors.	Class demonstration and discussion. Individual or paired investigation. PCP.	48

MATERIALS

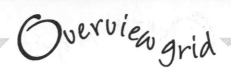
Learning objective	PoS/AO	Content	Type of activity	Page
Gases can be seen as bubbles when contained within liquid.	1e. *As above: Level B.*	Exploring bubbles. Collecting examples.	Class demonstration and discussion. Group investigation. PCP for recording.	50
Gases are produced when some materials are mixed together.	1e. *As above: Level C.*	Making and collecting gases.	Class introduction. Paired investigation.	51
Changing materials				
When materials are mixed changes can occur.	2a. *Materials from Earth: Level C.*	Testing a variety of materials with water.	Small groups investigating.	54
Heating some solid materials can cause changes which can be reversed by cooling.	2b, 2c. *As above: Level C.*	Heating different materials using hot water.	Small groups investigating. PCP for recording.	55
Heating some materials can cause changes which cannot be reversed by cooling.	2b, 2c. *As above: Level B.*	Heating foods for eating.	Small groups with adult supervision.	57
Cooling materials can cause them to change.	2b. *As above: Level B.*	Using a freezer to cool a variety of materials.	Whole-class activity or small groups. PCP for recording.	58
Temperature is a measure of how hot or cold things are.	2b. *Properties and Uses of Energy: Level B.*	School survey to investigate hot, warm, cool and cold areas.	Class introduction. Small groups to survey and report back. Class discussion. PCP for recording.	59
The instrument used to measure temperature is a thermometer.	2b. *As above: Level C.*	Examining, using and making a model of a thermometer.	Class introduction. Pairs investigating. Individual recording. PCP.	60
Cold temperatures can be measured.	2b. *As above: Level C.*	Measuring low temperatures.	Class discussion. Pairs investigating. Individual recording. PCP.	62
Hot temperatures can be measured.	2b. *As above: Level C.*	Measuring the highest safe temperatures.	Class discussion. Pairs investigating. Class discussion and research.	63
Freezing and melting are changes which can be reversed in many materials.	2c, 2d. *On Planet Earth: Level B.*	Exploring the freezing → melting → freezing processes.	Group investigation.	64
When a solid material dissolves in a liquid a change has occurred.	2a. *As above: Level B.*	Dissolving salt in water. Comparing with tap water.	Class demonstration.	66
Evaporation is a natural process.	2d. *As above: Level B.*	Exploring evaporation.	Whole-class discussion. Whole-class or group investigation. PCP for recording.	66
Different liquids evaporate at different rates.	2d. *As above: Level C.*	Evaporating different liquids.	Group or class investigation. PCP for recording.	68

11

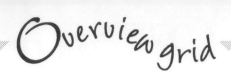

Learning objective	PoS/AO	Content	Type of activity	Page
Dissolving and evaporating are changes which can be reversed.	2c, 2d. *As above: Level C.*	Task completed by following instructions on dissolving and evaporating.	Individual or paired investigation. PCPs for instruction and recording.	69
Cooling causes condensation.	2d. *As above: Level C.*	Observing and exploring examples of condensation.	Class discussion. Individual investigation. PCP for recording.	70
Evaporation and condensation are changes which can be reversed.	2c, 2d. *As above: Level C.*	Exploring the cycle of boiling → condensing → boiling.	Class demonstration. PCP for recording.	72
Evaporation and condensation are natural processes in the water cycle.	2c, 2e. *As above: Level C.*	Exploring the water cycle.	Class introduction. Paired investigation. PCPs.	73
Changes which occur as a result of burning cannot be reversed.	2c, 2f. *As above, Level C.*	Burning different materials.	Class demonstration and discussion. Individual recording.	75
Separating mixtures				
A mixture can have particles of different sizes.	3a. *Materials from Earth: Level D.*	Making and sorting mixtures by hand.	Class discussion. Paired investigation. PCP.	78
Different-sized particles in a mixture can be separated by sieving.	3a. *As above: Level D.*	Separating the ingredients of mixtures by sieving.	Class discussion. Small-group investigation and demonstration.	79
Some solids dissolve in water.	3b. *As above: Level D.*	Testing materials for solubility.	Class demonstration. Pairs or small groups investigating. Class discussion. PCPs for recording.	80
An insoluble solid can be separated from the liquid by filtering.	3c. *As above: Level D.*	Filtering an insoluble material.	Class demonstration and discussion. Pairs or small groups investigating.	82
A dissolved solid can be recovered by evaporating the liquid in which it is dissolved.	3d. *As above: Level D.*	Reclaiming a dissolved material from a solution.	Class introduction. Pairs or small groups investigating.	83
There is a limit to the mass of solid that can dissolve in a certain amount of water.	3e. *As above: Level D.*	Making a saturated solution.	Class discussion. Pairs or small groups investigating. PCPs for recording.	84
The limit to the mass of solid which can dissolve in an amount of water is different for different solids.	3e. *As above: Level D.*	Comparing the amount of different solids which will dissolve in a given amount of water.	Class discussion. Pairs or small groups investigating.	86

Entries given in italics relate to the Scottish Science 5–14 National Guidelines.

Classifying materials

In this section, materials are examined and sorted and their properties are identified. Children are encouraged to take a closer look at familiar objects, to describe their appearance and texture, to carry out tests and investigations to discover the properties of materials, and to compare materials with each other.

Tests for hardness, strength, flexibility, reactions to water, magnetic behaviour, thermal insulation and magnetic attraction are described, as well as activities which encourage children to relate the properties of materials to the uses we make of them. Problems which we face through the excessive use of some materials, and through their disposal, are considered.

Activities to help children find out more about rocks and soils are provided. They are encouraged to observe these familiar materials closely, to carry out tests and to look for similarities and differences.

Children are also introduced to grouping materials according to whether they are solids, liquids or gases. Observations and tests will develop their awareness of the distinctive properties of solids, liquids and gases, and how these determine the ways we handle them and the uses that can be made of them.

Throughout this section, there are opportunities for first-hand experience; children can make detailed observations, predictions and comparisons and draw conclusions, thus furthering their knowledge and understanding of the properties of materials which influence their lives.

MATERIALS

■ SORTING MATERIALS

A wide variety of materials exists.

✝✝ *Brief instruction to whole class; groups of four or five arranged around tables for the activity, followed by discussion and whole-class activity.*

🕐 *45 minutes initially; could probably develop into an ongoing activity.*

Previous skills/knowledge needed

Pupils need to have an idea of how to group and sort familiar objects, and to be able to discuss and make comparisons as a group. They will need to know that everything around them can be sorted into 'things which are living' (animals and plants) and 'things which are not living', and that the objects they will be studying here will all belong to the non-living group. While engaged in this activity, children will be using their experience of the world and their senses.

Key background information

As our experience and understanding of the world develops, we begin to classify things into various groups or categories. Aristotle, a Greek who lived from 384–322 BC, was the first person who tried to explain that all things can be divided into their own groups and subgroups, and that we identify things we see by categorising them. If we decide something is living, we mentally put it in the plant or animal group; if it is non-living we start to place it in a different category. If we saw something completely new and we could not tell whether it was animal, plant or not living, we would be really puzzled. Children will understand that when we tidy a room we put things in a particular drawer or cupboard according to what they are. Aristotle attempted to tidy the world by his ordering of things.

Preparation

Assemble collections of objects. To avoid confusion, it is a good idea to organise the children into teams and the objects into groups.

Resources needed

A collection of about 12 familiar objects representing a range of materials, such as a pair of scissors, a plastic ruler, a duster, a cork, a wax crayon, a nail, a clay pot, a plastic pot, a paper towel, a piece of wood, a stone, a sock (each item should be made from one material only). One collection of objects could serve the whole class, but discussion and learning is more effective if each team has its own items to handle. Pieces of card or paper are needed by each team for labelling. Photocopiable sheet 102 (1 per child) and support sheet 103 (as required). Scissors are needed for the support activity sheet.

Sorting team	Number of groups we have sorted into	Names of our groups	Comments
Delia Robbie Jasvir Sean	4	soft hard paper plastic	We could rearrange into just 2 groups, soft and hard.
Kamaljit Mhairi Owen Belinda	2	will break easily / will not break easily	We could investigate our ideas another time.

Figure 1

What to do

Give each team the same assortment of objects. Explain to the children that they can sort these objects into groups in whatever way they choose. Encourage them to work together to discuss and decide on their criteria for sorting, writing the headings for the categories of objects on pieces of paper or card. Ten minutes is ample time for this part of the activity.

After sorting, allow each team in turn to explain the reasons for their groupings to the rest of the class. All criteria should be approved and briefly recorded at this stage, possibly as a blackboard summary. Depending on the age and abilities of the children, the ideas will range widely. Some of the more common groupings might include colour, texture, use, association and shape. Invite observations and comments: Are any groups very similar? Which category was chosen most often? Are there any groupings which could form the basis for an investigation at a later date (for example, the objects might have been sorted into 'those which break easily' and 'those which do not break easily')? It would be useful for each child to have a record of this activity, by making their own copy, or having a photocopy, of the teacher's recording. For a framework and example of how the sorting could evolve, see Figure 1.

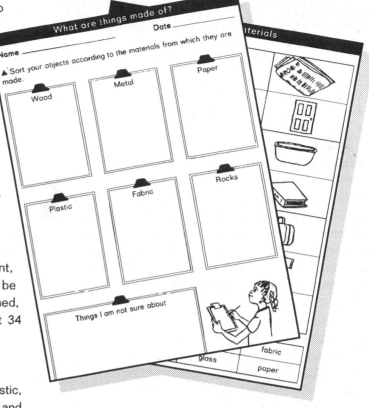

Next, ask the teams to rearrange their objects into groups according to the materials from which they are made. If any children have already done this, use their ideas to lead others on to this stage. Suggest a simple method of recording such as drawing circles or box shapes, or use photocopiable sheet 102, but it is important to allow individuality where it arises.

Encourage groups of children to make their own collections of objects and pictures (things made of wood, metal, plastic, fabrics, rocks, types of paper), showing variety within each group. A list could accompany each collection, explaining their common attributes.

Suggestion(s) for extension
As differences within groups of objects become evident, further sorting could be done. For example, wood might be in its natural state (hardwood or softwood) or be smoothed, polished, shaped or reconstituted. There are at least 34 different types of plastic in common use.

Suggestion(s) for support
Use photocopiable sheet 103; the headings metal, plastic, wood, and so on, can be cut out along with the names and pictures of objects made of these materials for the children to sort and arrange.

Assessment opportunities
Use the pictures and headings cut from photocopiable sheet 103 as a simple sorting task to see if children can identify objects and the materials from which they are made. Assess individual children's ability to respond to suggestions and work co-operatively within a group.

Opportunities for IT
As this is basically a sorting and 'hands on' activity, children should not be diverted from the main task by initially recording using IT. However, once the sorting has been completed, children might create a database which records their objects and the categories into which they have been sorted. If different groups of children have different objects, a larger class database could be created with each group adding their data. This would need some discussion over a common set of criteria.

Fieldnames might include:

Object	name of object
Material	plastic, wood, metal, paper...
Colour	selection of colours...
Mass	heavy, light...
Hardness	soft, hard...
Flexibility	rigid, bendy...

The activity would encourage children to think of other ways to describe hardness or flexibility. An alternative would be to use yes/no responses for some fields:

Hard	Yes/No
Flexible	Yes/No

The completed database could be used to answer such questions as:
Which objects are made of wood?
Which objects are made of wood and metal?
Which objects are hard and made of paper?

Display ideas
Provide new collections of objects on a regular basis for sorting. Supply small pieces of card for children to write labels for the new categories. Include pictures of large or unsafe items such as a glass vase, a piece of metal machinery, a car tyre or a plastic dustbin. Allocate areas around the room for children to arrange their collections of things made of wood, metal, plastic, and so on.

Other aspects of the Science PoS covered
Experimental and Investigative Science – 2b, c; 3a, b, e.

Reference to photocopiable sheets
Photocopiable sheet 102 provides an opportunity for children to list their objects according to the material from which they are made (extra objects can be added). Sheet 103 can be used for support or assessment.

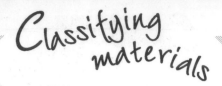

RECOGNISING MATERIALS

Materials have different properties.

†† *Brief instruction to the whole class, followed by group activity around tables. Six groups of three to five children will cover the materials described; adjustments will need to be made if you wish to involve a greater number of pupils. Whole-class discussion follows.*

🕐 *45 minutes, developing into an ongoing activity if possible.*

Previous skills/knowledge needed
Pupils need to have experience of sorting and grouping familiar objects and to be able to discuss and compare as a group.

Key background information
Children often begin to understand which materials are metal, plastic, paper, fabric, and so on, but do not ask themselves how they know this. Through examining, sorting and discussing, they can begin to understand that it is by the characteristics and properties of materials that we are able to recognise them.

Preparation
Make up collections of objects grouped according to the material from which they are made, (one collection for each group of children). Put the objects into plastic or paper carrier bags.

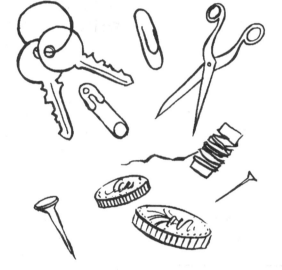

Resources needed
Objects to make up several collections of items made from metal, fabric, wood, plastic, rock and paper (rubber and glass could also be included if sufficient samples can be collected and made safe). The objects should be as wide-ranging as possible, providing a good workable collection. Hand-lenses would be useful, and a piece of card and felt-tipped pens are needed for each group. Photocopiable sheet 104 (1 for each child).

What to do
Give each group of children one collection of objects (all made of the same material). Tell them they are going to decide in what ways their objects are similar, making a list of the common characteristics on the piece of card provided. Allow about 15 minutes for group discussion and quick recording, and provide as little help as possible at this stage to encourage independent ideas. For children needing support, questions

to ask might include: Do the objects feel soft? In what ways do the objects look the same? Could you easily change the shape of the objects? Then allow each group to present their list to the rest of the class. Encourage children to share their ideas, looking for similarities and differences between collections, giving their reasons and comments. Which materials are considered strong? Which materials can be both soft and hard? Which materials cannot be bent?

Give each child a copy of photocopiable sheet 104 to record findings and the descriptions decided upon by each group. This can be done in stages as each group talks about their material, or completed afterwards – either from the cards filled in by the children during the activity, or from the blackboard if spelling is a problem. Colour-coding similar characteristics could be attempted by some children, using highlighting or shading methods to emphasise common words such as rough, smooth, hard or soft.

Finally, children can invent and test a sorting game to categorise 'new' objects – this could take the form of a 'yes/no' key.

Suggestion(s) for extension
Children can devise a blindfold test for each other to identify materials by touch only. Which materials are the easiest to recognise in this way, and which are more difficult because they are so similar? Can they explain how they know it is a piece of plastic they have in their hand rather than a piece of metal?

Many everyday items are made up of more than one common material. Children could use Venn diagrams to record information they collect about these items (see Figure 1).

Suggestion(s) for support
Write out the names of the items on small cards. Put them in one of the bags along with the collection of items. The children can use these cards to help with identifying and recording. Other cards can be used to provide descriptive words which the children can use as prompts to help them decide which words apply to their items.

Assessment opportunities
During group discussion, individual children's ability to make relevant observations can be assessed.

Opportunities for IT
Children could use a branching database to create an electronic key for identifying objects. To use this software, children must 'teach' the database differences between different objects by asking questions which have a 'yes/no'

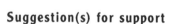

MATERIALS

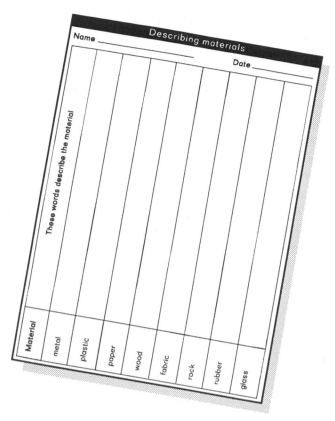

answer. The computer then creates a key which can be used by another child to identify any item included within the set of items. The creation of the key is an excellent language development activity. Younger pupils may need some assistance to start with in phrasing questions which require a 'yes/no' answer.

Different groups of children could create their own branching database and try it out with other groups.

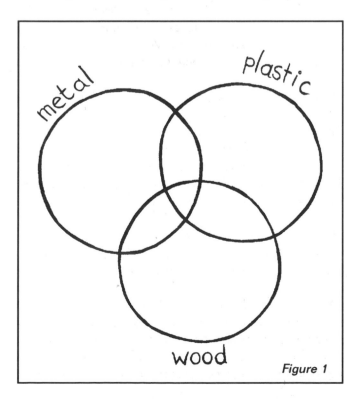

Figure 1

Display ideas

Ask each group of children to be responsible for a display of one type of material; the characteristics of the material should be written on cards and arranged alongside the objects. Words to go with *wood* might include 'smooth', 'strong', 'attractive', 'can be shaped'.

Other aspects of the Science PoS covered

Experimental and Investigative Science – 2b; 3a, b, c, e.

Reference to photocopiable sheets

Photocopiable sheet 104 provides a framework for collecting together each group's descriptions; completing this can be a shared and supportive task undertaken by all children. There are opportunities for children to extend their recording by means of colour coding.

HARD OR HARDER?

Some materials are harder than others.

✝✝ *Initial whole-class discussion, followed by testing in pairs or small groups.*

🕒 *15 minutes for discussion; 10 to 20 minutes for planning, organising and recording; 15 minutes for testing; 15 minutes to complete the recording; 15 minutes for reporting back to the class.*

⚠ *Adult supervision will be needed when the children are using the sharp-pointed tools.*

Previous skills/knowledge needed

Children will need to know the meaning of hardness and that a scratch is a mark that cannot be rubbed away. An introductory discussion can establish these facts.

Background information

One method of measuring hardness is a scratch test. A material's resistance to scratching or marking by other objects determines its hardness. In 1812, Friedrich Mohs, a German mineralogist, devised a system for measuring hardness using a scale from 1 to 10. He put talc at point 1, calcite at 3, quartz at 7 and diamond at 10. At 1 materials have a slippery feel, and at 2 they can be scratched by a fingernail. Materials of a hardness of 6 or greater cannot be scratched with a knife. This scale is still useful today although it has been extended, putting diamond at 15 to allow for the insertion between 10 and 15 of newly-developed artificial materials of extreme hardness.

Resources needed

A collection of materials for each group to test, such as two types of wood, a metal object (such as an aluminium can), two types of plastic, a piece of rubber, a pebble, a brick, a clay pot; tools with which to scratch the materials, such as a

think about their actual scratching technique, deciding as far as possible upon a fair and standard procedure.

Photocopiable sheet 105 will help children to organise their planning and set out their results. Each group can order their materials according to hardness – a material receiving the most scratches will be the least hard, the one marked by the fewest tools will be the hardest. Also consider the tools – the one which scratched the greatest number of objects will be made of the hardest material, while the tool having the least effect will be made of the softest material. Results can be presented orally to the rest of the class; comparisons can then be made and the methods and techniques used evaluated. Where there appear to be contradictions, children might suggest some retrialling.

A class hardness scale can be devised, giving each material tested a number or code as Mohs did. Other materials can be tested and given their place on this scale. Decisions will have to be made where doubts arise.

As a conclusion, ask the children to consider why people would need to know which materials are harder than others. They will have realised during this activity that tools must be harder than the materials on which they are used, and that surfaces need to resist the wear and tear of objects which regularly come into contact with them.

coin, a nail, a twig or a spent matchstick, a sharp piece of stone, a strip of plastic from a plant pot, a knitting needle; photocopiable sheet 105 and support sheet 106 (one copy per group).

What to do
Initiate a discussion to discover the children's ideas of what hardness is. Make sure that they are not confusing hardness with strength. This can be done by asking the children to look around the classroom and list objects or materials that they consider to be hard. Then ask them to give reasons and evidence to support their suggestions. How do we decide whether the window-pane is hard? How can we tell that the surface of the table is hard? Why do we describe a cushion as soft, which is the opposite of hard? Children will begin to realise that they are performing a simple but effective touch test to determine the hardness of materials and objects; the greater the resistance of a material to the pressure of their fingers, the harder it must be.

Briefly, make the distinction between hard and strong – a desk top and an eraser are both strong, but only the desk top is hard and strong. Encourage suggestions as to what might be a suitable test for determining the hardness of a material. How can the hardness of different materials be compared? Could other tools provide a more accurate classification than fingers? Lead on to the idea of scratching one material with another, with the result that the harder material will leave a mark on the other.

In groups, allow the children to organise, devise and record their own hardness tests on the materials provided. Where necessary, encourage the groups to plan a methodical working strategy in which everyone has a role to play. For example, in a group of four children, one pair could scratch all the objects with a nail and the other pair could use a spent matchstick to test the same objects. Children will need to

Suggestion(s) for extension
Children can research the use of tools in early times, looking at materials like bone, wood, stone, bronze and iron. They can collect and draw examples of tools and the materials they are used on, including sculptors' tools and kitchen tools.

Suggest carving a bar of soap to discover the best tools for the job – try plastic cutlery, sharpened twigs and tools used for clay work.

Suggestion(s) for support
It might be necessary to limit the number of tools used, in order to simplify the task. Photocopiable sheet 106 offers a simpler method of recording.

Assessment opportunities
As groups are carrying out this activity, observe the children's ability to provide explanations and record their observations. At the end, create an oral or written quiz to test the children's understanding of hardness and their skill at selecting the right tool for the job.

Opportunities for IT
Children could use a word processor to write the labels for a class display on 'hardness'. A large version of the hardness scale could be presented using a word processor. Some children could be given an opportunity to record their work using a word processor, possibly for inclusion in the display. Try to allow children to originate their work at the computer rather than retyping handwritten work.

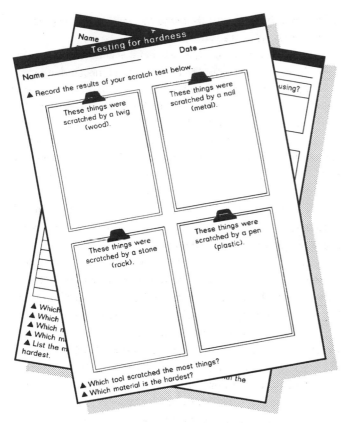

Name _____
Testing for hardness
Date _____

Name _____
▲ Record the results of your scratch test below.

These things were
scratched by a twig
(wood).

These things were
scratched by a nail
(metal).

These things were
scratched by a stone
(rock).

These things were
scratched by a pen
(plastic).

▲ Which
▲ Which
▲ Which m
▲ Which m
▲ List the m
hardest.

▲ Which tool scratched the most things?
▲ Which material is the hardest?

Display ideas

Create a large visual representation of the class hardness code, with space to write in all materials tested. If this is displayed horizontally, the materials themselves can be placed at the appropriate points along the line. Collect tools used for working wood and metal, along with examples of the material they are used on. Display carvings or pictures of work by sculptors. Provide a block of wood or soft stone for the children to try out carving techniques using various tools.

Other aspects of the Science PoS covered

Experimental and Investigative Science – 1a, b, c, e; 2a, b, c; 3a, b, c, d, e.

Reference to photocopiable sheets

Photocopiable sheet 105 offers a framework for recording if required, including a table for the results of the testing. Sheet 106 offers a simpler recording framework.

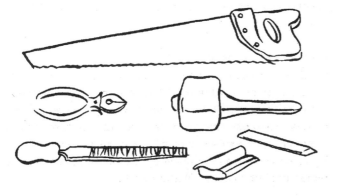

STRONG OR STRONGER?

Some materials are stronger than others.
†† _Preliminary whole-class discussion and observation followed by paired activity. Pairs can report back and discuss findings with the rest of the class._
🕐 _20–30 minutes for discussion and observational activity; 45 minutes for testing and recording._

Previous skills/knowledge needed

Children will have their own ideas of what strength is from their experiences of handling and using different materials. They will make the general assumptions that metal is stronger than paper, and plastic is stronger than wood; but they may not have considered the strengths of different types of paper, plastic, wood or metal, or compared the strength of two materials which have the same use.

Key background information

The strength of a material relates to how tough it is (resistant to breaking or tearing), how well it will resist the forces of other materials and to what extent it will support heavy loads. We rely on the strength of materials to create bridges, buildings, machinery, ships and planes as well as everyday items such as boxes and furniture.

Preparation

Collect a variety of papers such as tissue-paper, kitchen roll, newspaper, pages from magazines, different writing papers, gift wrapping paper, brown paper, and art papers. Cut these into small pieces (approx. 12cm × 10cm) and allow for each pair to have two pieces of each type. It might be helpful to give each type of paper a code number for easy reference.

Resources needed

A clipboard for each child; quantities of different types of paper; photocopiable sheets 107 (1 per child) and 108 (1 per child).

What to do

Begin by asking the class to tell you what they think being strong means in scientific terms. All relevant suggestions can be written briefly on to a blackboard or flip chart, perhaps in two groups – words associated with strength such as tough, supporting or resisting, and words indicating the qualities strong materials do not show, such as bending, tearing or breaking.

Tell the children that they are going to make a list of materials that exhibit strength. Provide each child with a clipboard and plain paper (or use photocopiable sheet 108), and either make a tour of the school and its surroundings or find a spot where many examples can easily be found. Encourage the children to make quick sketches of the objects they find and label their observations, examining a good variety of different materials. Examples could include door frames, shelves and a tree trunk (wood), car bodies and waste-bins (metal), walls (brick and rock), chairs and boxes (plastic), school bags and clothing (fabric). Discussion during and after this activity will generate and extend ideas and allow comparisons to be made.

Move on to comparing the strengths of different types of one particular material. Give each pair of children the small pieces of different papers prepared earlier. First, ask the children to arrange these pieces according to how strong they think they are, making a note of their decisions using the name or code number (see above) of each paper type. Photocopiable sheet 108 can be used for the recording. When this is done, ask the children how they could carry out a simple test to see how strong the papers really are. Suggestions might include tearing or pushing a pencil point through each paper. Decide upon a class strategy and determine some standard and safe techniques, such as the method of tearing or piercing each type of paper. Recording of methods should take place at this point before the testing is done. If possible, allow each pair to try two different tests to confirm the results and to extend discussion. The children should make decisions and physically order their paper samples as they test them, completing their recording sheets at the end of the task.

Testing for strength

Name _____ Date _____

What we want to find out.

What we are using.

This is our prediction of the order of strength.

Test one	Test two
This is what we will do.	This is what we will do.
Our results:	Our results:

▲ Which paper have you decided is the strongest?
▲ Which paper have you decided is the least strong?
▲ Is this what you expected?

Suggestion(s) for extension

Encourage children to compare the strength of plastic cutlery with its metal equivalent. A test could involve eating all meals for a number of days with a set of plastic tools, making comments on difficulties encountered with different foods.

Children can use books to find and draw examples of constructions where the strength of a material is vitally important – roads, bridges, buildings of various types. Ask them to consider why we do not fall through floors.

Suggestion(s) for support

With the introductory activity, work closely with children who have difficulty observing, asking them questions relating to the immediate surroundings. Where can you see metal being used for its strength? Why do we need a strong piece of wood over the doorway? What would happen if the table-top were made of sponge? During the testing activity, some children might need guidance when ordering their paper samples. Allow plenty of working space and encourage a methodical sorting procedure.

Assessment opportunities

While the children are working, there is an opportunity to assess their observational skills and ability to organise a simple test, make decisions, record results and draw conclusions.

Display ideas

Use the children's annotated sketches and write out key words such as 'strong', 'stronger', 'strongest', 'strength' and 'support', in large lettering for easy reference. After the testing, arrange the different papers in order of their strength according to the class decision.

Other aspects of the Science PoS covered

Experimental and Investigative Science – 1a, b, c, d; 2a, c; 3a, b, c, d, e.

Reference to photocopiable sheets

Photocopiable sheet 108 can be used for recording observations in the form either of words or of annotated drawings, while sheet 107 provides a framework for recording the test and its results.

BEING FLEXIBLE

Some materials are more flexible than others.

†† *Whole-class discussion, followed by children working individually or in pairs.*

🕐 *20 minutes for discussion; 20–30 minutes to complete the activity sheet; 30–40 minutes for testing and recording.*

Previous skills/knowledge needed
This activity builds on and extends children's previous experience of materials which bend.

Key background information
Materials which are flexible can be folded, twisted, wrapped around things or bent. When a piece of material is bent, the outer edge must stretch while the inner edge is compressed. Squeezing a sponge shows how a material is stretched and compressed. Some materials are only flexible because of their thinness; aluminium is extremely flexible when it is used to make foil, less so when it is used to make cans. The opposite of *flexible* is *rigid* or *stiff*. Flexible materials can be folded easily and are good for wrapping; rigid materials are needed for building solid structures. Materials which are completely flexible return to their original shape after bending.

Preparation
A few days before this activity introduce the concept of flexibility to the children and suggest that they make a collection of flexible objects. Be ready to provide flexible items of your own, if necessary.

Resources needed
Everyday items of varying degrees of flexibility including elastic bands, plastic tubing, different sorts of paper, aluminium foil, a leather belt, pieces of fabric, wire, string, cardboard, a Swiss roll, clingfilm, sponge, and so on; Photocopiable recording sheet 109 (one copy per child).

What to do
Display the collection of flexible objects to promote discussion. Examine the items as a class, deciding why each one is flexible and asking for suggestions as to how they could be sorted. Eventually, group the items according to the materials from which they are made. Some of these groups will have many more items than others; perhaps the children can suggest reasons for this. Photocopiable sheet 109 can be used for recording.

Encourage the children to devise a simple test for flexibility. It could involve twisting or wrapping materials around a pencil or cylinder, or around angular objects such as a small cube or larger box. Observations and comments can be made on the ability of each material to fit the contours of the shape. Finally, discuss the usefulness of flexibility in a material, as well as instances where flexibility would be disastrous. Children can record their ideas as amusing drawings showing flexibility where it is not needed. For example: walking on a floor or bridge, putting a heavy load on a table, trying to close a door.

Suggestion(s) for extension
What is the opposite of flexible? Children could investigate this also. Make a list of instances where stiffness or rigidity in a material is very important.

Suggestion(s) for support
Write labels for each item in the flexible materials collection, or make an alphabetical list so that where necessary, children can refer to the names for recording purposes.

Assessment opportunities
Children's completed versions of photocopiable sheet 109 will help when assessing their understanding of the property of flexibility.

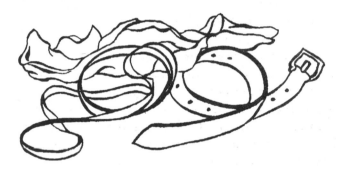

Opportunities for IT
Children could use a word processor or desktop publishing package to make labels for the class display on 'flexibility'. They could explore the use of suitable fonts and styles to create a more interesting display. Some children might be able to create more interesting labels using a graphics package which allows the text to be twisted, stretched or bent to highlight the concept of flexibility.

The teacher could prepare a file containing the names of all the objects being explored in a jumbled order. The children could be asked to sort the list into order of flexibility using the knowledge they have gained. The activity would provide an opportunity for children to learn how to move words around the screen using the 'cut and paste' or 'drag and drop' facility. This could also be used as part of an assessment activity for understanding of both science and IT.

Display ideas
Develop the collection of flexible things and make it available for hands-on testing. Encourage the children to make labels describing the flexible nature of particularly interesting items and indicating their usefulness. Display children's amusing drawings which show flexibility where it is not needed.

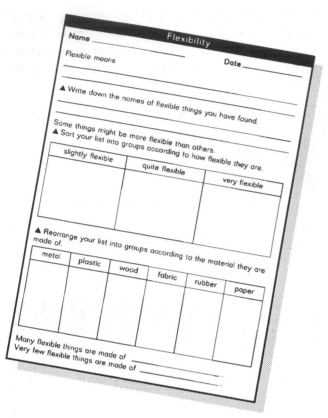

Other aspects of the Science PoS covered

Experimental and Investigative Science – 1a, b, c, d, e; 2a, b, c; 3a, b, c, d, e.

Reference to photocopiable sheet

Photocopiable sheet 109 provides a framework for children to record their understanding and results.

⬒ FLOATING AND SINKING

Some materials float in water; others sink.

†† *This lesson could be a whole-class demonstration, with as many children as possible taking part, or a group activity. Depending on the resources and space available, groups could work simultaneously or in turn.*

🕐 *10 minutes for prediction; 30–40 minutes for testing and recording; 10 minutes for reporting back.*

Previous skills/knowledge needed

Most children will be aware of the concepts of floating and sinking and will need to make careful observations to clarify their ideas.

Key background information

The upthrust force of water keeps some things afloat. Other things which are more dense push against this force and are able to sink. Some materials float lower in water than others, depending on their density. Where amounts of air are contained within a material or object, this increases its buoyancy. If a sponge is immersed in water, the air gradually rises to the water's surface as bubbles, and the sponge then sinks as it becomes waterlogged. Stability is important in keeping air in and around a floating object.

Resources needed

At least one large transparent container; a variety of objects which can be tested for buoyancy, including items of different materials and shapes – include a sponge, an empty box with lid, a blown-up balloon, and two balls of Plasticine (of approximately the same size); photocopiable recording sheet 110 (1 copy per child).

What to do

Display the items to be tested and ask the children to predict whether they will float or sink. Show the children the two equal-sized balls of Plasticine and ask someone to change the shape of one ball, moulding it like a saucer before testing.

Discussions can involve the whole class; but decisions should be made individually, with children preparing their own chart for recording or, alternatively, using the framework provided by photocopiable sheet 110. Once the children have made their predictions, let them carry out the testing in groups or allow individuals to demonstrate to the rest of the class. Point out that each item must be placed carefully on the water in the same way, and that observations and comments for each should be recorded accurately.

Discussion during and after testing will raise relevant questions: Does all wood float? Does the shape of an object affect its buoyancy? What part does air play in keeping things afloat? Is stability a factor in floating?

Suggestion(s) for extension

Issue a challenge: Can the children make things which normally float, sink, and things which normally sink, float?

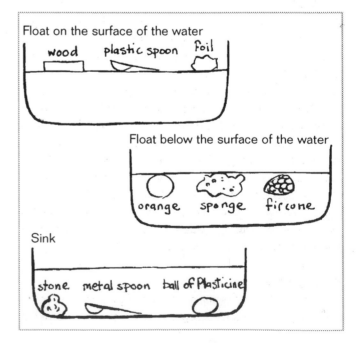

▲ Which things will float and which will sink?				My observations	My comments
Things we are testing	My predictions: will float/will sink/not sure				

Name

Floating and sinking

Date

for testing their boat designs. Draw a large cross-section outline of the container, showing the water level. Children can attach drawings of the objects tested to show the positions at which they rested in the water. Appropriate vocabulary can be displayed.

Other aspects of the Science PoS covered
Experimental and Investigative Science – 1a, b, c; 2a, b, c; 3a, b, c, d, e.
Physical Processes – 2g.

Reference to photocopiable sheet
Photocopiable sheet 110 provides a chart for recording the children's predictions, observations and comments.

Design and test model boats. Pay attention to stability and the loading of cargo. Find out about the Plimsoll Line on ships.

Suggestion(s) for support
Photocopiable sheet 110 provides help with recording; or alternatively, children can present their observations in diagrammatic form (as shown on page 22), using three large shapes to group objects which sink, objects which float on the water and objects which float just below the surface.

Assessment opportunities
The suggestions for extension will help to assess, where necessary, a child's ability to apply the experience that has been acquired of floating and sinking, to science in everyday life.

Opportunities for IT
Children could use an encyclopaedia CD-ROM to search for information on floating-related subjects like Plimsoll, the Dead Sea or ice-bergs. Children could retrieve the text from the CD-ROM and add pictures to create their own short article on the topic – perhaps combining pictures from other CD-ROMs, clipart collections, scanned from their own hand-drawn illustrations or drawn with an art or graphics package.

Older children might set up an electronic quiz using multimedia authoring software. Each new screen could show a different object and children will be asked to click on one of three answers: float, sink, float underwater. Selecting the correct answer would lead the child to the next object, a wrong answer might provide a picture of what happens to the object once placed in water.

Display ideas
Have a suitable container of water available for testing the buoyancy of new items brought in by the children, as well as

SOAKING UP WATER

Some materials soak up more water than others.
†† *Whole class for introductory session; children working in pairs for the test; whole-class reporting of results and discussion afterwards.*
🕐 *One hour.*

Previous skills/knowledge needed
Children will need to be able to work successfully with a partner, use a dropper accurately, and count and record meticulously.

Key background information
Materials vary as to how much water, or other liquids, they can absorb. The water replaces any air the material contains as well as clinging to its surfaces.

Preparation
Cut small pieces of the same size from a variety of fabrics, so that a good spread of results can be achieved.

Resources needed
For each pair of children: a hand-lens, a small transparent jar, an elastic band, a small dropper, a container of water; small pieces of fabric cut to the same size from a variety of fabrics; photocopiable sheet 111.

What to do
Divide the children into pairs and provide each pair with a jar, small pieces of fabric, an elastic band and a dropper. Withhold the water until the planning is complete. Explain that they are going to see how much water the pieces of fabric will soak up before any water starts to drip through. They will test this by fixing a piece of cloth evenly over the top of the jar using the elastic band. Then, drop by drop, they will add water on to the surface of the cloth until the water drips through into the jar. Allow time for a close examination of

the fabric using a hand-lens, and for careful planning of the stages involved in the test; so that each pair knows exactly what will be happening and how they will be sharing the task efficiently.

The children must count and record the number of drops applied to the fabric before a single drop of water hits the bottom of the jar. The jars must be completely dry before each test. Use photocopiable sheet 111 for recording.

Figure 1 shows the investigation. Each pair could test a different fabric but it is useful if each type of fabric is tested more than once (for checking purposes).

Check each pair's strategy before allowing the test to proceed. Questions to ask could include:

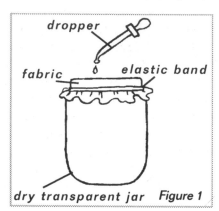

dropper

fabric   elastic band

dry transparent jar   Figure 1

What method are you using to make sure you remember how many drops have been applied to your cloth sample? Who is counting and who is dropping the water? What do you have to be especially careful about?

After all the tests are completed, compare results and arrange the fabrics in order according to their ability to hold water. Ask which cloth the children would recommend for mopping up spillages.

Suggestion(s) for extension

Investigate whether it is possible to prevent fabric from absorbing water.
A test might include rubbing the cloth with candle wax and then carrying out the water drop test again.

Encourage a group of children to plan an investigation which tests a variety of cloths for their ability to mop up water.

Suggestions(s) for support

Children might need help to record the number of drops as they proceed. They could use the reverse side of their recording sheet or photocopiable sheet 111 for this. They should write each number as they apply the drops. In this way, they are less likely to lose count than when using a tally system.

Assessment opportunities

Assess the children's ability to plan and organise a given task, sharing the work and operating efficiently and fairly.

Opportunities for IT

Children can display the results of this work using a simple graphing package. They could enter the name of the fabric and the number of drops added before water dripped through. The package would enable them to sort the data to display the graph alphabetically according to the name of the material, or numerically by the number of drops added. The data could also be displayed in different forms and the value and relevance of the formats discussed.

Children could also record their results using a simple spreadsheet. It could be set up with a row for each material tested and then the number of drops needed. If children test the same material several times, the spreadsheet can be used to average out the results. The spreadsheet could be set up in advance and the computer positioned so that children could enter their results directly on to the spreadsheet during the testing. Children could use their results to plot graphs displaying their work. The spreadsheet might look like this:

Fabric	try 1	try 2	try 3	mean
Cotton	10	15	16	10.33
Wool	22	24	23	23
Nylon				

Children could also discuss the benefits of using software for this type of work against more traditional longhand approaches.

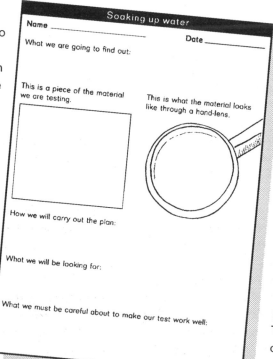

Soaking up water

Name _____

Date _____

What we are going to find out:

This is a piece of the material we are testing.

This is what the material looks like through a hand-lens.

How we will carry out the plan:

What we will be looking for:

What we must be careful about to make our test work well:

Display ideas

Group the materials tested with appropriate labelling to show their water-absorbing properties. Make a collection of cleaning and mopping cloths for the children to examine.

Other aspects of the Science PoS covered

Experimental and Investigative Science – 1a, c, d; 2a, b, c; 3a, b, c, e.

Reference to photocopiable sheets

Photocopiable sheet 111 provides a planning framework for the activity. There is a space for a small piece of the material which is being tested to be attached by staple or adhesive tape, as well as a space for a close-up drawing of the fibre arrangement as seen through a hand-lens.

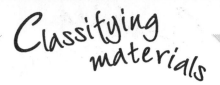

MAGNETIC MATERIALS

Some materials respond to magnetic forces.

†† *Children working in pairs.*

🕐 *20–30 minutes for initial test and recording; allow several days for the collecting of metals, followed by 45 minutes for the second test and recording. Extra time might be necessary for research.*

Previous skills/knowledge needed

Children will be familiar with magnets and their forces of attraction from everyday experience; their greater understanding of magnetic forces will depend on coverage of Physical Processes (Forces and motion) in school. Children must know how to handle magnets properly. Dropping or heating magnets can cause a loss of magnetic properties. They should be made aware that magnets must be kept away from watches and electronic equipment and need to be stored carefully to preserve their magnetism.

Key background information

All materials attracted to a magnet are metal, but not all metals are attracted to a magnet. Most items attracted to a magnet will contain iron. The molecules in a magnet are arranged in a strict pattern, all of them lined up in the same direction. Each molecule is itself a tiny magnet. In a non-magnetised but magnetic material, the molecules also behave like tiny magnets – but they are arranged haphazardly. When a magnet exerts a 'pull' on such a magnetic material, it causes the molecules of that material to arrange themselves in a similar regimented pattern

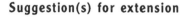

to that in the magnet. A magnet can lose its magnetic strength if dropped, as the molecules become disarranged. To remagnetise it, a damaged magnet can be stroked several times in one direction by another magnet to reorganise the molecules.

Preparation

Check magnets; collect materials to be tested.

Resources needed

A collection of different magnets (bar, horseshoe and circular types, fridge magnets and magnets from games). For the first test, use a variety of non-metal items such as a plastic counter, pieces of wood, rubber, string, fabric, and a paper tissue, as well as a few metal items such as a paper-clip, a piece of wire, a key and a coin. For the second test, familiar and unusual items can be collected together with the help of the class to provide a well-varied selection. (Turnings and shavings from engineering works are interesting, and the metal is more easily

identifiable.) If available, a set of named metal discs will be useful in discovering exactly which metals show magnetic behaviour. A timer or watch; copies of photocopiable sheet 112.

What to do

Provide a range of items for testing with magnets and ask the children to predict whether there will be an attraction between the magnet and each material. What will happen when each item is placed next to the magnet? Will the magnet pull the item towards it? Perhaps nothing will happen at all. Give the children photocopiable sheet 112 to record their predictions on, allowing for some extra items of their own choice to be added. Next, give each pair a magnet to check their predictions and encourage them to fill in the recording sheet. Finally, the children can practice sorting a mixture of plastic counters and paper-clips using a magnet and compare this with the time taken by a hand-sorting method.

Ask the children to help collect a range of metal items for testing with magnets. Each pair will need to use the same magnet for each test, as all magnets vary in strength. Children should group the items according to the degree of magnetic behaviour. Some metals will not be attracted at all, some will show a weak attraction, others a stronger one. By examining each group which should contain several items made of the same metal, children will be able to make observations and deductions. If named metal discs are available, these can be used to help identify metals in the collection. Explain that metals containing iron will exhibit magnetic properties and that steel consists largely of iron. Recording can be carried out individually, with children devising their own scale of magnetic attraction. Examples of the usefulness of magnetic behaviour can be collected.

Suggestion(s) for extension

Children can do further research into the magnetic attraction of metals.

Ask the children to invent a game which makes use of magnetic attraction.

Collect used drink cans for recycling. Children can check their metal content with magnets to distinguish between steel and aluminium cans.

Suggestion(s) for support

Photocopiable sheet 112 offers support with recording; symbols and drawings can be used where necessary. The names of metals can be written on cards to be used as a word bank.

Assessment opportunities

Check the children's ability to use equipment correctly. Devise a simple quiz to show the children's understanding of the relationship between non-metals and a magnet, as well as the behaviour of different types of metals and magnets.

Opportunities for IT

Older children might set up an electronic quiz using multimedia authoring software. Each new screen would provide an object and children could be asked to select the right answer for the question on the screen. Selecting the correct answer would lead the child to the next object, a wrong answer might provide an explanation of why the material is, or isn't attracted to a magnet.

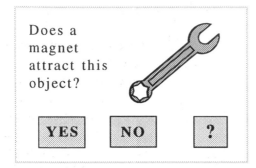

Does a magnet attract this object?

| YES | NO | ? |

Display ideas

Create a 'hands-on' area featuring different types of magnets and a growing collection of items to test. An accompanying chart should be provided for children to record their observations. Make a Scale of Magnetic Attraction: stretch out a piece of string on which children can attach the items they have tested, ordering them according to the degree of magnetic attraction they have shown. Alternatively, the names and drawings of the items can be written on cards and fastened to the string.

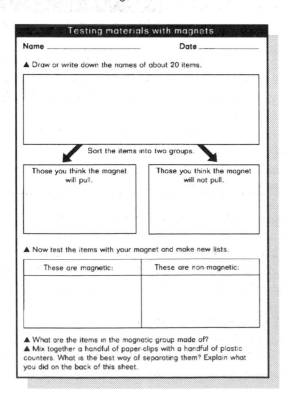

Testing materials with magnets

Name _____ Date _____

▲ Draw or write down the names of about 20 items.

Sort the items into two groups.

| Those you think the magnet will pull. | Those you think the magnet will not pull. |

▲ Now test the items with your magnet and make new lists.

| These are magnetic: | These are non-magnetic: |

▲ What are the items in the magnetic group made of?
▲ Mix together a handful of paper-clips with a handful of plastic counters. What is the best way of separating them? Explain what you did on the back of this sheet.

Other aspects of the Science PoS covered

Experimental and Investigative Science – 1a, b, c, d, e; 2a, b, c; 3b, c, d, e.
Physical Processes – 2a.

Reference to photocopiable sheets

Photocopiable sheet 112 allows for recording of the children's predictions and the results of the testing. The time trials for the sorting challenge can be recorded on the reverse of the sheet.

ESCAPING HEAT

Heat travels from a warmer to a cooler material.
†† *A whole-class activity with discussion and recording.*
🕐 *30–40 minutes.*
⚠ *Care needs to be taken when touching hot objects.*

Previous skills/knowledge needed

Children will know that they can detect the temperature of objects by touch, although they might not realise that the heat is passing to or from their skin. They need to know that *hot* is the opposite of *cold* and *cool* is the opposite of *warm*.

Key background information

Heat is always trying to escape (by conduction, convection or radiation) to a cooler place. When anything we touch feels cold, the heat is passing from our hand; when anything feels hot, heat is passing to our hand. Conduction is the process whereby heat passes between materials that are touching each other.

Resources needed

Photocopiable sheet 113 (one per child).

What to do

The first part of this session should be done quite quickly, within ten minutes, and the children need to jot down their findings prior to more permanent recording. Ask the children to decide whether their hands are cold, cool, warm or hot. This, of course, will vary according to the temperature and their previous activity. Then suggest that they look around the room and find three or more things which feel warmer than their hands, and three or more things which feel cooler. This information can be transferred to photocopiable sheet 113, which also provides the opportunity to record the date, season, weather conditions and indoor and outdoor temperatures if these are available. Discuss why things feel hot or cold and explain that heat always tends to escape by moving from a warmer material to a cooler material, and this is known as *conduction*.

Create opposite scenarios, where one person is cold and trying to warm up by finding hot things to touch, and another is hot and is touching cooler things in an attempt to keep cool. Children may suggest warming up by hugging radiators, hot water bottles and each other, clasping mugs of hot drinks and taking a hot bath. Use this opportunity to emphasise the dangers of hot substances and the risk of burning. Children might consider cooling themselves by using cold water or ice cubes on their skin and leaning against a cold wall.

Finally, children can transfer their ideas on to the second part of the photocopiable sheet.

Suggestion(s) for extension

Collect examples of hot things which are used to warm up colder things, such as an electric blanket. Suggest that the children feel the temperature of their chair seats after sitting, and ask them where the heat has come from.

Encourage the children to collect further instances where we try to hasten the passing of heat from a hot (or warm) material to a cold one. They might suggest using ice or a bag of frozen peas to soothe an injury and cool the skin, or putting food in a refrigerator. (Warn children that hot food should be allowed to cool down to room temperature before being refrigerated, to avoid warming up other food in the refrigerator.)

Suggestion(s) for support

The activities on photocopiable sheet 113 can be simplified for less able children.

Assessment opportunities

The second part of photocopiable sheet 113 can be used to check that children understand that heat always travels from a warmer to a cooler material.

Figure 1

Display ideas

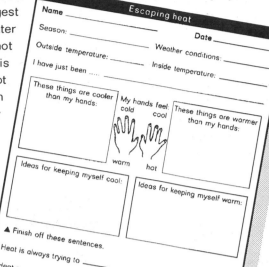

With the children's help, create opposite scenarios which show heat transfer, one where escaping heat is a problem and one where it is welcomed. Figure 1 shows an example.

Other aspects of the Science PoS covered

Experimental and Investigative Science – 1b, c; 2b; 3b, c, d, e.

Reference to photocopiable sheets

Photocopiable sheet 113 offers a framework for recording information collected. The date, the weather conditions and the activity the child has recently been involved in will influence how warm or cool things feel, and should be recorded. Children can circle the appropriate word to describe the temperature of their hands and colour-code the boxes to illustrate warmth and coolness. A simple assessment exercise completes the sheet; children are asked to draw in the arrowheads to show the direction heat is travelling.

TRAVELLING HEAT

Some materials conduct heat more effectively than others.

†† *Children can organise the task in groups; alternatively, one demonstration can be carried out for the whole class, with all children having the opportunity to take part.*

🕐 *15 minutes for initial discussion; 45 minutes for planning, testing and recording.*

⚠ *Precautions should be taken when dealing with hot water and hot objects.*

Previous skills/knowledge needed

If children have been introduced to the concept that all things are made up of very tiny particles called molecules, they will understand more easily that heat energy travels through materials by the vibration of these molecules.

Key background information

If heat travels easily through a material, that material is a good conductor of heat; if heat does not pass easily through it, that material is a bad conductor. In materials which are good conductors of heat, the molecules of which the material is composed vibrate vigorously as they warm up and pass heat from one to the next very quickly; in a bad conductor, the molecules are less affected by heat, vibrate only a little and therefore little heat is passed on.

Preparation
Safe access to a supply of hot water is required.

Resources needed
Spoons, or similar items, made from different materials (wood, plastic, metal); a stable container for the hot water (a glass jug, if carefully handled, is ideal as children can see the spoons during the test).

What to do
Start off with a discussion to remind the children that heat always tends to escape from its source, and that heat moves from a warmer material to a cooler material by conduction.

To demonstrate the conduction of heat through a material, tell the children that they each represent a molecule of an object and that you are a source of heat. The children will need to be sitting together fairly closely in the class, or be gathered together to form the shape of a rectangle or an oval. The effect will probably be more easily observed by the children if they are seated. As the source of heat approaches the nearest molecule, that molecule begins to vibrate as heat energy is transferred to it – encourage the nearest child to you to jiggle about but to remain in the same spot. In turn, this causes the neighbouring molecules to start moving – the children in closest contact with the first molecule begin to move in a similar way. This pattern continues until the heat is passed through the whole object – the whole class.

This would be the reaction of a material which is a very good conductor of heat. The molecules of a bad conductor would only be affected by the heat slowly; there would be less vibrating and little movement passed on and so most children would remain still. (See Figure 1.)

Try this several times, changing the shape of the group of children and each time announcing whether they are molecules of a good conductor or of a poor conductor of

heat and varying the point at which the source of heat approaches the object.

Next, show the children three or more similar items made of different materials, such as a wooden spoon, a plastic spoon and a metal spoon, or a wooden, a plastic and a metal ruler. Ask for ideas for finding out which of these is made of the best material for conducting heat. Suggestions might involve putting the items next to a source of heat energy like a radiator, and testing by feel to find out which ones have absorbed any heat. Be prepared to try out any workable and safe ideas.

A simple demonstration to show how heat is conducted through these different materials uses hot water. Explain to the children that the items you are using, for example spoons, have been chosen because they are similar – that is, approximately the same length, thickness, and so on. These items will be put (end-on) into a jug half-filled with hot water and left to stand for a while. Ask the children what they think will happen. What will happen to the heat in the water? Will it travel along the items which are in contact with the water? Will the rate at which the heat travels be the same? How will they know which materials conduct heat?

Give the children an opportunity to record the plan. Then put the spoons in the hot water. After about three minutes, invite a child to feel the dry end of each spoon very carefully and to report to the rest of the class. By this time, there should be a warming of the end of the metal spoon. Other children can test and compare the ends of the spoons at regular intervals, bearing in mind that too much handling can cause the spoons to become warm. If necessary, repeat the test so that each child has a chance to decide on the temperature of the spoon handles. The metal spoon will prove to be the best conductor of heat, warming steadily and then losing its heat as the water cools. The plastic and wooden spoons should remain quite cool. Discuss the different uses of spoons in the kitchen and how this is related to the material from which they are made.

Items with the most noticeable temperature change demonstrate good conduction; those which have hardly changed have been least affected by the heat and are bad conductors. The children can record their findings.

Molecules of a good conductor of heat   *Molecules of a poor conductor of heat*

source of heat   *source of heat*   *Figure 1*

Suggestion(s) for extension
Encourage the children to devise tests for other materials – paper, rock, ceramics, cork, other metals. These could safely be put next to a radiator or left out in the sun for a short time (check both the top and the underside of the objects).

Suggestion(s) for support
Where necessary, give help with recording by providing headings or an outline drawing which children can mark or colour code.

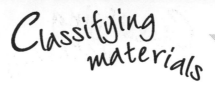

Assessment opportunities

Children's conclusions to this investigation should give an indication of their understanding of the process of conduction of heat through everyday materials.

Display ideas

Make available items which children can sort into groups according to whether they are good conductors or bad conductors of heat. Children can create lists which can be extended as new discoveries are made. Display items made of a material specially chosen because it conducts heat easily, for example a copper-bottomed saucepan.

Other aspects of the Science PoS covered

Experimental and Investigative Science – 1a, b, c, d, e; 2a, b, c; 3a, b, c, d, e.

HOLDING ON TO HEAT

Materials which are bad conductors of heat are good insulators of heat.

†† *Whole-class introductory discussion. If the weather is cold enough, groups of children can set up their tests outside using their own collection of materials and will thus have a greater chance of handling the items and making their own decisions. If a refrigerator is being used it might be necessary to use one group of materials for the whole class, or allow groups to use the refrigerator in turn.*

🕐 *15 minutes for introduction and organising the test; 45 minutes for recording and checking the results.*

Previous skills/knowledge needed

Children should know that heat travels from a warmer to a cooler material by a process called *conduction*.

Key background information

Materials which are good conductors of heat are bad insulators. Good insulators are useful in preventing heat from escaping too rapidly.

Preparation

If space in a refrigerator or freezer is not available, choose a very cold day for this demonstration. Collect a range of building materials.

Resources needed

Building materials such as different types of brick, pieces of different woods, polythene, polystyrene, metal, glass, also paper and card; photocopiable sheet 114 (one per child).

What to do

Ask the class to help you collect a variety of building materials; relatives engaged in DIY activities or involved in the building trade will usually supply small samples, including recently-developed insulating materials, and this should provide a useful range for testing.

An introductory discussion will remind the children that some materials allow heat to travel through them more quickly than others. Explain that you are going to investigate which materials are best for preventing heat from escaping when used for building purposes. Put the materials outside on a very cold day, or place them in a refrigerator for about 20 minutes. While waiting, ask the children to describe the investigation they are carrying out, and make a chart to show the results. Use photocopiable sheet 114 if appropriate.

After about 20 minutes the children should be able to make a decision about each material – whether it feels slightly cold, cold or very cold. The very cold materials will have lost most of their heat; those which do not feel so cold will still be retaining some of their heat. The materials should be examined as quickly as possible before any rise in temperature is brought about by handling or by the effect of room temperature. Materials which have been put outside at cold temperatures can probably be examined out of doors.

When each group has completed the results chart, allow time for comment and comparison. Explain that the materials which feel the coldest will have lost the most heat. Those which feel less cold have retained some of their heat, and are therefore useful when heat needs to be prevented from escaping. Tell the children that these materials are called *insulators*. Arrange the materials in groups according to how the children have rated their insulation properties.

Suggestion(s) for extension

Encourage a group of children to devise and plan an investigation to make a more accurate comparison of the insulating properties of materials used in building.

Collect advertising literature and invite an expert to the school to talk about methods of home insulation.

Suggestion(s) for support

Make name cards for the building materials which are being tested, to help children complete their recording sheets more easily.

Assessment opportunities

Children might be able to suggest and carry out an independent investigation leading on from this activity. This will show their understanding of the properties of insulators and conductors.

Display ideas

Make the building materials available for children to examine more closely; provide a hand-lens and name cards so that the correct terminology becomes familiar to the children.

Other aspects of the Science PoS covered

Experimental and Investigative Science – 1a, c; 2b, c; 3a, b, c, e.

Reference to photocopiable sheet

Photocopiable sheet 114 provides questions to assist with planning, as well as a chart for recording the decisions the children make after feeling the materials.

KEEPING WARM AT HOME AND SCHOOL

Materials which are good thermal insulators are useful for keeping things warm.

✛ *Depending on numbers of children, school organisation and arrangement of buildings, children could work as a large group, in smaller groups or in pairs. If this activity could take place during a cold weather spell, the importance of insulating materials in keeping a building warm would become even more evident.*

🕐 *20–30 minutes class session; 30 minutes (and possibly longer) for survey; one hour for reporting back and recording.*

Previous skills/knowledge needed

Children will need to be aware that heat is always moving from its source to colder areas, and they can be reminded of this in the introductory discussion. They will need to be able to use a simple plan to find their way around school, devise and use a key and record information on a plan.

Key background information

Materials which keep heat in during the winter and out during the summer are ideal for building. Doors and windows can cause problems by letting heat escape on cold days; energy-saving measures such as thick curtains, double glazing and draught excluders (which could be called heat retainers) are useful for preventing heat loss.

Preparation

Decide on the parts of the school that you want the children to survey, trying to include areas where they will find a good range of examples. Photocopy school plans (one for each pair to use during the survey, and one for every child to have for final recording).

Resources needed

A simple plan of the school buildings; clipboards. Experts such as the caretaker, parents in the building trade and representatives of energy conservation groups are excellent contacts.

What to do

Help the children to imagine their school on a very cold day, as a source of heat energy amidst the coldness of the outside world. Ask them to close their eyes while you describe a winter scene of intense frost, snow and icy winds, giving specific details relevant to the school's immediate surroundings. Then start to mention the efforts made by the caretaker to keep the school warm. Describe the interior of the building as a warm oasis amidst a cold desert.

Encourage each child to draw a simple representation of

the school building, including symbols or words to indicate all the heat sources inside. (See Figure 1 for an example.) They will think of radiators, any other heaters and even themselves. Remind everyone that this heat is always trying to escape and let them annotate their drawings of the building to show this, thinking of all the ways that heat could get out. This will encourage them to look in all directions, and consider walls, ceilings and floors, when they carry out the following survey.

Now organise a survey of the school (either the whole or specific parts), providing each group with a clipboard and plan of the area you want them to survey. Tell the children to search for actual examples of where they think heat could be escaping. This will involve going outside to look at roof areas and other external structures and the materials of which these are made. Allow 20 to 30 minutes for this, so that children can report back to you and their findings can be checked. Further time might be needed, depending on the area to be covered.

to record their findings. Encourage the use of a key and a system of colour coding. Doors, windows, skylights, curtains, and sources of heat should be marked, as well as the different materials used for walls and roofs.

Finally, ask the children to help compile a list of suggestions for keeping heat within the school, some of which could probably be implemented. Encourage the children to make out a report sheet to communicate their findings, and include a list of recommendations for preventing heat loss from the buildings.

Suggestion(s) for extension

Encourage children to carry out a similar survey of their home.

Make a collection of building materials, examine them closely and then predict which ones might be good thermal insulators. Devise ways of finding out.

Considering what they have found out about heat escaping from buildings, ask the children to design a 'Building of the Future'.

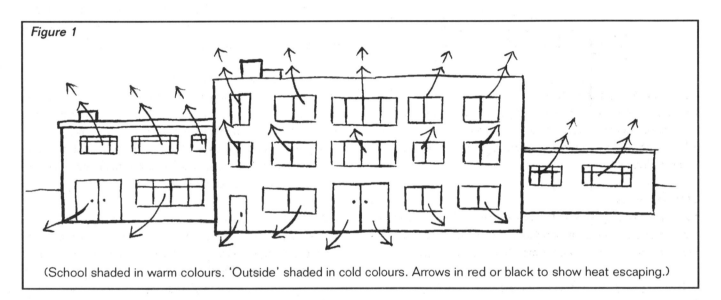

Figure 1

(School shaded in warm colours. 'Outside' shaded in cold colours. Arrows in red or black to show heat escaping.)

Provide an opportunity for groups to report back to each other; in this instance, groups could pair up and share their information prior to a whole-class discussion.

Important points to look out for include:
▲ What have the children used to determine in which places heat is being lost? The easiest way is for them to use their bodies as a temperature indicator and make judgements as to how hot or cold they feel.
▲ Which materials do they think are letting the most heat escape?
▲ Which materials do they think are best at keeping the heat in the school?
▲ Where are the worst spots in the school for heat escaping?
▲ Is there any evidence of people trying to use extra materials to stop escaping heat? (There might be examples of energy conservation measures.)

Give the children another plan of the school on to which

Suggestion(s) for support

Limit the survey to one room. Draw a simple plan and encourage the children to look at the materials of the walls, floor and ceiling, touching where possible. Provide a code sheet which will help children to organise the filling-in of their plan using symbols.

Assessment opportunities

This activity provides the opportunity to focus on children's ability to organise a task and relate the information collected to a genuine practical purpose.

Opportunities for IT

Children could use a graphics package to draw a plan of the school and mark on the sources and 'losses' of heat, perhaps using red for sources and blue for losses. This would involve children in selecting different colours, filling shapes, drawing

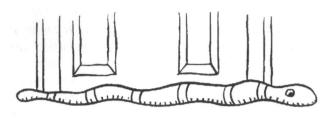

lines, and so on. They could use thick or thin coloured lines to represent good and bad sources or losses of heat.

Alternatively, they could use a plan previously prepared by the teacher which they load into the graphics package to draw in the hot and cold spots as above. Children who make a survey of their own home, or a room inside it, could use the graphics package to draw a plan of their home or room and mark on the sources and losses of heat.

This activity could also be used to introduce some simple measuring using hand-held electronic thermometers to record the temperature. Children could check the temperature around windows, doors and walls outside the building to see where the temperature is greatest. The advantage of an electronic thermometer is the speed and accuracy of the reading available.

Display ideas
Create a large plan of the school to display in a prominent position so that it can be seen by everyone; show the proposals for keeping the school warm on this. Give the class the opportunity to present the results of their survey and suggestions for implementation of their ideas to an assembly of the whole school.

Other aspects of the Science PoS covered
Experimental and Investigative Science – 1b, c; 2b, c; 3a, b, c, d, e.

THERMAL INSULATORS IN THE KITCHEN

Materials which are thermal insulators are useful at home.

†† *Whole-class discussion and brainstorming, with individual recording.*

🕐 *15 minutes for discussion and 20–30 minutes for recording.*

Previous skills/knowledge needed
Children will need to understand the terms *conduction* and *insulation*.

Key background information
The kitchen is an ideal focus for examples of thermal insulation, as well as providing examples of the conduction of heat. The uses of materials which demonstrate these properties can be identified and compared.

Resources needed
A collection of kitchen items would be useful to refer to when discussing the kitchen scene; photocopiable sheet 115 (one copy per child).

What to do
Give each child a copy of the kitchen scene on photocopiable sheet 115. Discuss the examples of thermal insulation that can be seen: plastic handle on saucepan, wooden spoon and spatula, plastic kettle jug, ceramic mug for hot drink, vegetable dish with lid, oven gloves... Provide the opportunity for the children to annotate the pictures, describing the examples and their specific purposes. Encourage them to think of an idea for an investigation, while they are doing this, to compare the insulation properties of different materials.

Suggestion(s) for extension
Use the children's ideas to plan an investigation. (See the chapter on Investigations.)

Find out how a haybox can be used in the cooking of food.

Suggestion(s) for support
The preliminary discussion will help children to develop their understanding of the concept of thermal insulation. Where necessary, ask prompt questions relating to the picture as the children complete their sheets: Which part of the saucepan is safest to touch? What material is it made of? What can be used to get a hot dish out of the oven?

Assessment opportunities
Observe the children's ability to apply their knowledge and understanding of thermal insulation to everyday equipment.

Opportunities for IT
Children could use a word processor to write labels for a display of kitchen objects. They could experiment with fonts of different styles and sizes or introduce the idea of coloured fonts to illustrate the degree of thermal insulation provided: red letters for good insulators and blue for poor. Different shades (orange, yellow, and so on) could be used to make a scale of thermal insulation.

Display ideas
Arrange the kitchen items for close examination; children can write labels to highlight the thermal properties of the materials from which the items are made.

Other aspects of the Science PoS covered
Experimental and Investigative Science – 2b; 3b, c, e.

Thermal insulators in the kitchen

▲ Find examples of thermal insulation in this picture.

Reference to photocopiable sheets
Photocopiable sheet 115 shows an illustration of a kitchen with a number of examples of the use of thermal insulation. Children can recognise these and write comments around the picture.

KEEPING OURSELVES WARM

Clothing is important in keeping us warm and is often designed to take advantage of the insulation properties of air.

†† *Whole-class discussion, followed by children working individually or in pairs.*

🕐 *45 minutes for the task itself.*

Previous skills/knowledge needed
Children will need to understand the meaning of *insulation*.

Key background information
Many fabrics designed for warmth take advantage of the insulation properties of air – hairy fibres, loose weaves and large stitches in knitted fabrics are all methods for trapping air in fabric. Similarly, air trapped between layers of fabric provides warmth by preventing loss of heat from the body. The air outside our clothes does not insulate us so well because it is not still: it can move around, thus taking heat away from our bodies.

Preparation
Fill a large plastic bag with clothes – some obviously for winter wear, some for summer wear, and some items which will need to be considered more carefully. Collect a wide range of fabrics, factory offcuts or pieces from old clothes, and cut these into samples – some large enough for examination, and smaller pieces of the same fabrics for the children to attach to their recording sheets.

Resources needed
A variety of fabric pieces; hand-lenses; photocopiable sheet 116 (one per child).

What to do
Let the children help you sort the bag of clothing into winter and summer garments, then ask them how they decided what was suitable for each season. Suggestions might include thickness, fluffiness, and perhaps colour. Continue this theme by providing small samples of various fabrics for the children to examine with a hand-lens. Give every child two examples of fabrics designed for summer and for winter wear, then ask them to write descriptions of the fabrics and make drawings of the threads (when magnified) on photocopiable sheet 116.

Discuss the common properties of those fabrics which children have predicted will keep them the warmest. Lead them to consider the part played by air trapped between the fibres, which acts as a barrier in preventing our body heat from escaping.

Encourage children to think about ideas for an investigation to find out which types of fabric keep us the warmest or for a test to see if several layers of thin fabric are more efficient in keeping us warm than one thick layer.

Suggestion(s) for extension
Study the clothes chosen by explorers and people who live in cold areas of the world.

Find out how animals keep warm. Examine and test feathers, look closely at fur and research the behaviour of creatures that live in arctic climates.

Ask two children to compare the insulation properties of two different pairs of gloves. Each child could wear one glove from each pair and spend some time outside (probably for a breaktime on a cold day), discovering which hand is kept warmer. In this way, each child would monitor the other to make sure the test was fair and no other factors were introduced.

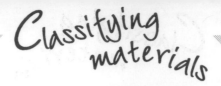

Suggestion(s) for support

Provide help for children who have difficulty describing the fabric samples; write key words and clues on cards for children to select when they are recording.

Assessment opportunities

Check individual children's ability to choose a material for a particular purpose, according to its insulation properties.

Opportunities for IT

Children could use a word processor to write labels for a display of different fabrics. They could experiment with fonts of different styles and sizes or introduce the idea of coloured fonts to illustrate the degree of thermal insulation provided: red letters for good insulators and blue for poor. Different shades (orange, yellow, and so on) could be used to represent fabrics between these two extremes!

Display ideas

Create two contrasting areas – 'Staying Warm' and 'Keeping Cool' – where children can display winter and summer fabrics and clothes with labels, promoting the advantages of each.

Other aspects of the Science PoS covered

Experimental and Investigative Science – 1a; 2a, b; 3b, c, e.

Reference to photocopiable sheet

Photocopiable sheet 116 provides children with a framework for recording observations they make when closely examining different fabrics. Samples of the fabrics can be fastened to

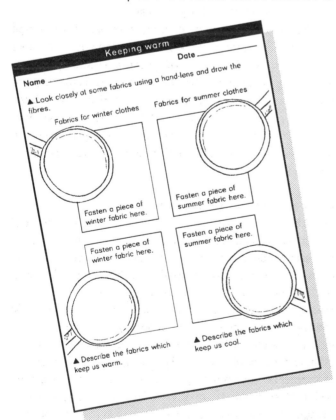

the areas indicated, and close-up drawings of the fibres can be sketched in the magnifying glass shapes. The reverse of the sheet could be used for children to draw and label a variety of winter and summer clothes before attaching their fabric samples to the photocopied side and writing descriptions of them.

MATERIALS CONDUCTING ELECTRICITY

Some materials are better at conducting electricity than others.

†† *Whole class introduction, followed by children working in pairs or small groups depending on the availability of resources.*

🕐 *One hour.*

Previous skills/knowledge needed

Children will need to have explored the flow of electricity around a circuit using a battery, bulb and wire. They will need to know how to set up a complete circuit in order to light a bulb.

Key background information

Metals are usually good electrical conductors. Most other materials resist the flow of electricity through them and can be used as insulators. Graphite, the 'lead' in a pencil, is a non-metal through which electricity will flow easily.

Resources needed

For each pair or group: equipment to make a circuit including wire, a bulb and bulb holder, a compatible battery, crocodile clips (a small screwdriver and wire-cutters might be needed), a range of materials and items for testing; photocopiable sheet 117 (one copy per child).

What to do

Remind the children how to set up a circuit with the equipment provided, but tell them to include a gap in the circuit which can be closed by two crocodile clips. When the circuit has been tested, tell the children that you want them to find out which materials electricity can pass through. Children may suggest using different materials and objects to bridge the gap when the crocodile clips are parted. Photocopiable sheet 117 can be used to record results. Items provided for testing could include a key, a coin, a pencil, plastic items, aluminium foil, paper, paper-clips, and so on; but allow the children a free choice to give the greatest variety. Sometimes the bulb will appear bright and sometimes dim, while at other times it will not light at all.

The children will be able to decide which materials are the best conductors of electricity. Questions to ask could include:

Why does the bulb not light up when a plastic cube is bridging the gap? Why are paper-clips useful to complete a circuit? Are all metals equally good at conducting electricity?

Discuss the importance of conductors for passing electricity from one location to another, and the importance of materials which do not allow electricity to pass through them and can thus be used as insulators. Highlight the dangers of using mains electricity and the need for correct use of insulation materials.

Suggestion(s) for extension

Encourage children to list instances in which materials are used to conduct electricity (copper for wires and lightning conductors), as well as examples of materials being used because of their properties of insulation (such as rubber and plastic for plugs and wire coverings).

Suggestion(s) for support

For some children it might be necessary to write on the chart the names of the items which are being tested.

Assessment opportunities

Devise a simple oral or written quiz to determine whether a child understands which materials are important for conducting electricity and which ones are needed for insulation against electricity.

Display ideas

Make circuit-making equipment available so that the children can continue to test materials as they think of them. All things tested should be added to the list.

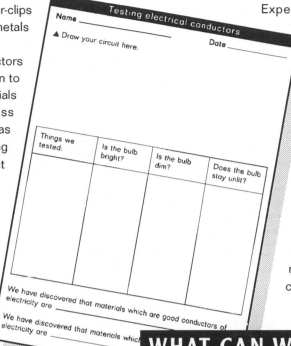

Testing electrical conductors

Name _____
▲ Draw your circuit here.　　Date _____

Things we tested:	Is the bulb bright?	Is the bulb dim?	Does the bulb stay unlit?

We have discovered that materials which are good conductors of electricity are _____
We have discovered that materials which _____ electricity are _____

Other aspects of the Science PoS covered

Experimental and Investigative Science – 1a, b, c, d, e; 2a, b, c; 3a, b, c, d, e.

Reference to photocopiable sheet

Photocopiable sheet 117 provides a framework for recording. Children can draw their circuit and complete the chart as they test, then record a short summary of their findings. The reverse of the sheet can be used to record the uses that can be made of materials which are good or bad conductors of electricity.

WHAT CAN WE DO WITH NATURAL MATERIALS?

Natural materials can be changed for people to use.
†† *Initial teacher-led discussion using items collected; children working individually when recording, discussing in groups if necessary.*
⊕ *45 minutes with extra time for research.*

Previous skills/knowledge needed

Children will be drawing on their experience and knowledge to clarify their ideas, develop understanding and make connections, so the lesson will proceed according to age, ability and experience. Children will need to know that the term *manufactured* usually refers to something having been worked upon and changed, probably by machinery; and that the term *artificial (or man-made)* generally indicates a substitute or newly-developed material provided by more complicated means.

Key background information

There is no simple distinction between natural and artificial things; every object is ultimately made from a product of the earth, although some things have been contrived more than others by humans. Anything gathered directly from the earth is a raw material. Then there are those things which have merely been shaped by hand or machine from natural materials – for instance, a wooden door, a gold ring or a woollen sock. Other things have undergone a more complicated, possibly chemical process, and it is often difficult to know from what they originally came – for instance a plastic ball, a glass bowl, a sweatshirt. The more complicated a product is the more stages there will be in its manufacture.

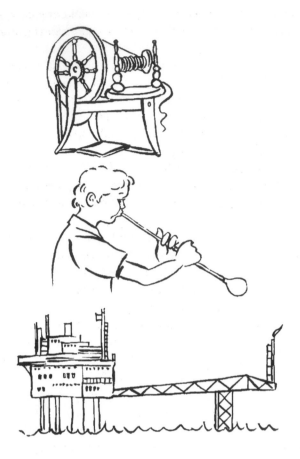

industry but are not necessarily in their final state. Ask the children if any of these can be connected with the first group (the ball of wool and the fleece, the brick and the clay, and so on). When all likely connections have been made, ask if anyone can suggest a further stage in the life of these materials. Finally, produce some of the end products so that children can complete the stages in the production process, for example fleece → wool → jumper. Recording can take the form of drawings and words linked by arrows, with children choosing and mapping the materials which interest them the most.

Ask the children if they think any important everyday things have been missed out, for example, glass and plastic items (if these have not already been mentioned in discussions). Point out that it is impossible from just looking at the end product to get any idea of the origins of a pane of glass, a plastic bag or a pair of tights. Briefly explain that glass is made using a process involving sand and other materials, and that oil is the basis of all forms of plastic and many artificial fibres. Children can research the production of glass, plastic and fibres and include them on their recording page.

Suggestion(s) for extension
Encourage the children to look more closely at fibres. Let them examine labels on each other's clothing to find out exactly what the fibres are made of. Discover what is the most common fabric being used at the moment.

Make a flow chart which shows the many different types of plastic which are made.

Suggestion(s) for support
Where it is necessary, restrict the examples so that children can concentrate on the less complicated processes. Write the appropriate vocabulary and draw arrows on cards for children to arrange, instead of recording them individually.

Assessment opportunities
Devise a simple quiz or game which will indicate children's understanding of the processes involved.

Opportunities for IT
Children might be able to use an encyclopaedia CD-ROM to research information on the different materials. They could also create a multimedia quiz similar to that in 'Floating and sinking' on page 23.

Display ideas
Encourage children to seek out unusual items to create a display showing natural materials and those which have been altered by human industry. Write out and display the names which have been invented for artificial materials.

Other aspects of the Science PoS covered
Experimental and Investigative Science – 2b; 3b, c, e.

Resources needed
A range of natural items in raw material form (a lump of rock, some clay, a small branch, a pile of sand, a shell, some rain water, a handful of natural sheep's fleece which could be collected from fences and hedgerows, or can be obtained from a farm or a local spinners' and weavers' group); a range of items which have been partly altered by hand or machine (a wood offcut, a ball of wool, a piece of chalk, a brick, a piece of copper wire, a piece of cut stone); a range of items which have been manufactured from natural materials (a woollen jumper, a spoon, rubber balloons, a piece of jewellery); a range of items which bear little resemblance to the materials from which they were originally made (for example a nylon sock, a plastic bowl and a glass jar). Pictures are useful to illustrate the process of obtaining crude oil, gathering latex for rubber production, mining ores and glass and plastic production. Appropriate books will be needed for research.

What to do
Allow all the class to examine the collection of natural items. Ask them to decide what they all have in common. Through comment and discussion it should become evident that these are completely natural things, produced on the earth with little interference from people. Discuss what it would be possible to use them for. Next, show them the natural materials which have been shaped in some way by human

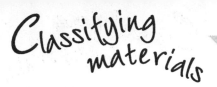

CHOOSING THE RIGHT MATERIAL

The properties of a material determine its use.

†† *Initial whole-class discussion, followed by children working in pairs or individually.*

🕐 *40 minutes to one hour, depending on how many different items the children examine.*

Previous skills/knowledge needed

Pupils will need to have handled, tested and investigated a wide variety of materials, and be familiar with and understand the properties of these materials (see the previous activities in this chapter).

Key background information

The most suitable material is chosen for a particular purpose; however, cost, availability and appearance also need to be taken into account. A material like plastic can be made to imitate a traditionally-used natural material such as wood. The use we make of the Earth's resources is a matter of increasing concern, and we are also faced with the problem of disposing of unwanted materials which have already been used.

Preparation

Select a piece of equipment for initial stimulus discussion and extra items and pictures for the children to work with.

Resources needed

Objects and pieces of equipment in regular use which children can safely examine (such as a saucepan, a kettle, a thermometer, coins, an incubator, various boxes and containers), together with pictures of larger pieces of equipment like a car, a plane or a piece of machinery or furniture; photocopiable sheet 118 (assessment, as required), and 119 (extension, as required).

What to do

First introduce an interesting piece of equipment and ask the class what it is made of. Start with something simple like a saucepan which is probably made of just two materials. Then ask why these materials have been chosen. Direct the discussion so that children are connecting the material with its properties and its use. Why has a type of plastic been chosen to make the handle of this saucepan? Why hasn't the same material been used as for the pan? What might happen if metal had been used for the handle or plastic for the pan?

Then let the children examine other items themselves, discussing their ideas with a partner and recording their findings.

Move on to more complex items. A door might have a panel of glass being used for its transparent property, enabling people to look through and light to enter a room; wood for strength and hardness; and metal parts such as hinges, handles and locks used for their strength and because metal is able to be moulded and hammered into shape. A bicycle has tyres made of rubber because of its flexibility; a metal frame for strength; and the seat and other parts made of plastic because it is lightweight and can be moulded into shape.

Ask questions relating to strength, hardness, flexibility, durability; whether the materials have been used because they are waterproof or light in weight; whether they demonstrate the properties of thermal insulation, magnetic attraction, or electrical conductivity.

The relative cost of materials, and whether they are attractive in appearance and/or easily available, could also be considered.

Suggestion(s) for extension

A complex item could be drawn and the parts labelled and annotated to create an informative display.

Encourage a debate, to be illustrated in cartoon form, as to whether a £5 coin would be more useful than a note. Children might compare the weight of a number of coins and notes, durability, handling (especially by visually impaired people), usefulness in vending machines, and so on.

Introduce the words *biodegradable* and *sustainable*, *durable* and *renewable*, and discuss how these properties apply to materials such as wood, metal and plastic. Use photocopiable sheet 119, which encourages children to think of materials in terms of the way we use them, whether supplies will run out and the problems of created waste.

Children can invent a story character who always uses the wrong materials with disastrous consequences.

Suggestion(s) for support

Write key words on small cards which children can attach to the items or pictures they are examining and use later to help with recording.

Assessment opportunities

Using photocopiable sheet 118, children need to show that they can select the materials that would be used to make particular objects and give reasons for their decisions.

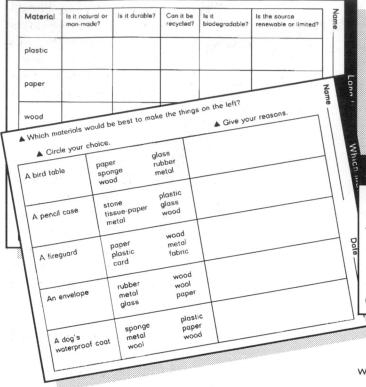

Material	Is it natural or man-made?	Is it durable?	Can it be recycled?	Is it biodegradable?	Is the source renewable or limited?
plastic					
paper					
wood					

▲ Which materials would be best to make the things on the left?

▲ Give your reasons.

▲ Circle your choice.

A bird table	paper sponge wood	glass rubber metal	
A pencil case	stone tissue-paper metal	plastic glass wood	
A fireguard	paper plastic card	wood metal fabric	
An envelope	rubber metal glass	wood wool paper	
A dog's waterproof coat	sponge metal wool	plastic paper wood	

Reference to photocopiable sheets
Photocopiable sheet 118 is an extension task which will initiate discussion and require research, and could lead to independent investigations. Encourage more detailed comments rather than 'yes/no' answers. Sheet 119 can be used to assess a child's ability to choose the right material and give reasons for the choices.

A CLOSE LOOK AT ROCKS

Types of rock are different from each other in their appearance and texture.

†† *A whole-class discussion prior to the activity will help children to work more purposefully. If sufficient resources are available, children can work in pairs to observe and record.*

🕐 *One hour.*

Previous skills/knowledge needed
Children will need to be able to work successfully with a partner, sharing information.

Key background information
Rocks vary according to how they were formed. Sedimentary rocks are usually softer and gritty, and often contain evidence of plant and animal life in the form of fossils; igneous and metamorphic rocks are harder and can contain crystals.

Preparation
Make sure that you have collected enough rock samples to keep every child busy; it might take some time to build up a suitable collection of rocks. If the children are asked to help with the collecting, then a greater variety will be achieved. They can find unusual rocks on their travels, as well as useful pieces where roads and pathways are being made.

Resources needed
Hand-lenses; a rock collection consisting of as many different kinds of rocks as possible; photocopiable sheets 120 (one per child) and 121 (as required for support).

What to do
Divide the class into pairs and provide each pair with samples of rocks and a hand-lens. Tell them they are going to find out as much as possible by closely examining each rock. Ask for suggestions from the class as to what they might discover. The class discussion should include ideas on: colour – encourage a description of the overall colour as well as a detailed close examination; texture – ask children to close their eyes, pressing and rubbing the rock's surface to discover whether it feels soft or firm, smooth or gritty; whether there is evidence of fossils or the presence of crystals; if the rock is uniform in consistency or varied. Give out copies of

Opportunities for IT
Children could work in pairs to select one of the materials and create an annotated drawing of the material using either an art or graphics package. The picture could be drawn by the children using the software, taken from clipart collections or scanned from their own hand drawings. Text can be added and linking lines drawn to add information about the different materials.

Display ideas
Arrange objects and pictures with detachable labels for matching activities as well as children's work which develops from the class activities.

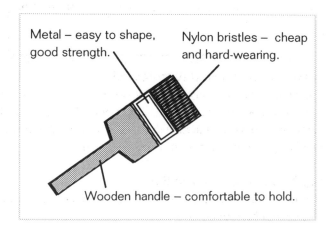

Metal – easy to shape, good strength.

Nylon bristles – cheap and hard-wearing.

Wooden handle – comfortable to hold.

Other aspects of the Science PoS covered
Experimental and Investigative Science – 2b; 3a, b, e.

photocopiable sheet 120, which consists of a chart and a small word bank (or sheet 121 if required for support). Rocks can be exchanged until everyone has completed their chart. As rocks can be difficult to recognise and identify, they should be numbered or coded in some way so that the children will know which pieces they have examined.

Suggest comparing rocks with other pairs; can any similarities be found to link certain samples? What sort of groupings could be made? Encourage the children to group the class rock collection according to criteria they think are important. They might decide on hard and soft rocks, or rocks with fossils and those without or the rocks might be grouped according to colour.

Suggestion(s) for extension
Using reference books, together with knowledge of where the rocks were found, it might be possible to find the names of some of the samples. Research on the uses of rocks can be linked to what has been discovered by observation and handling.

Suggestion(s) for support
Photocopiable sheet 121 provides a chart which can be used to record the children's observations by using ticks or other symbols.

Assessment opportunities
Check the accuracy of children's descriptions to assess their ability to describe and observe.

Opportunities for IT
Children could use an encyclopaedia or specialist geology CD-ROM to look up information on the rocks. Once all of the rocks have been identified, children could create an electronic key using branching database software. To use this software the children must 'teach' the database differences between different rocks by asking questions which have a 'yes/no' answer. The computer then creates a key which can be used by another child to identify any rock whose details have been entered into the software. The creation of the key is an excellent observation and language development activity. As

many rocks are very similar in appearance, it would be sensible to begin with a small set of rocks with obvious differences between them. Other rocks can always be added later.

Display ideas
Arrange the rocks with informative labels made by the children. Allow the children to group and regroup them according to different characteristics. Use pictures showing different uses for rocks.

Other aspects of the Science PoS covered
Experimental and Investigative Science – 2a, b, c; 3a, b.

Reference to photocopiable sheets
Photocopiable sheet 120 provides a framework within which children can record their observations of the rocks they examine. The observations of four rocks can be recorded on the sheet; children can continue on the reverse side with further observations. A bank of words is supplied. Sheet 121 reduces the need for written observations and consists of a chart on which children can make marks for recording purposes.

ROCK HARD

Some rocks are harder than others.

†† *Whole-class introductory discussion followed by children working in pairs.*

🕐 *One hour.*

Previous skills/knowledge needed
If children have already tested a variety of materials for hardness they will understand more readily the meaning of hardness and ways of testing this property, and will probably need only a brief reminder of what is involved.

Key background information
Harder rocks will scratch softer ones. A scratch is a mark that cannot be rubbed away.

The harder the rock, the more useful it is for buildings and pathways; consider the durability of the marble used for the Parthenon and the stone used for Hadrian's Wall. Softer rocks are easier to carve and grind; talcum powder is derived from soft rock, and lime is obtained by grinding limestone.

Preparation
Build up a collection of small pieces of rock.

Resources needed
Tools for scratching (nails, coins, a sharp twig and sandpaper can be tried); a variety of small rock pieces (some of which are soft like sandstone and limestone, and others which will resist scratching such as flint and granite). Provide enough pieces for each pair to be able to test several samples.

What to do
A preliminary discussion will remind children what hardness means and how it can be tested. (See 'Hard and harder'.) Tell the children that they will be working in pairs to devise a scratching plan using any of the tools supplied – they will need to make judgements so they can arrange their rocks in order of hardness. As a check, each rock can be used as a tool to scratch its neighbour in the line-up, a softer rock always being marked by a harder one.

Recording can take the form of a 'Hardness Line' featuring simple drawings and brief descriptions together with names if known. (See illustration below.)

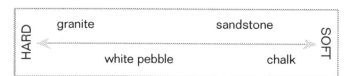

Children can compare their results with others, so that a class 'Hardness Line' can be devised. This could involve arranging the rocks in order of hardness, or stretching out a piece of string or rope to which labels can be attached. Some retesting might be required if any doubts arise.

Suggestion(s) for extension
Use books to discover the uses of hard and soft rocks. What kinds of tools are needed for cutting rocks?

Suggestion(s) for support
Provide guidance where necessary when the children are devising the test. Recording can take the form of a tick list devised to include the rocks and the tools available for testing.

Assessment opportunities
Check the children's skills of organising, observing and ordering.

Opportunities for IT
Children could use a word processor or desktop publishing package to make labels for a 'hardness line' compiled by the whole class.

Display ideas
Encourage the children to present their 'Rock Hardness Line' with rock samples and labels for everyone to see.

Other aspects of the Science PoS covered
Experimental and Investigative Science – 1a, b, c, d, e; 2a, b, c; 3a, b, c, d, e.

PERMEABILITY

Water can pass through some rocks more easily than through others.

†† *Whole-class discussion and brainstorming of ideas, followed by pairs working as part of a whole-class activity.*

🕐 *One and a half hours.*

Previous skills/knowledge needed
Children will need to have some ideas about how to plan an investigation; since this is done as a class activity individuals can support each other and be reminded of the need for consistency and fair testing.

Key background information
Some rocks are more permeable than others. Rocks with air spaces can take up water; those which are denser will cause water to run off them.

Resources needed
A collection of rocks including some which will take up water (such as chalk, sandstone and limestone), and some which will not, (such as granite, flint and marble); droppers; a small container of water for each pair.

What to do
Explain to the class that you want to find out what happens to rain when it falls on rocks. Children will suggest that it will either run off or soak in. Ask for ideas about how this can be investigated using the class rock collection. Give pairs of children a few minutes to discuss and then pool ideas. One workable suggestion would be to use droppers, putting one drop at a time on the surface of each rock and making careful observations. Encourage the children to provide a class set of instructions which they must all use and stick to. Write these on the board as they are suggested, changing and adapting as necessary. When everyone is happy with the final plan (having thought about how carefully the drops will be applied, what counts as run-off, and when the test will be over), the instructions should be copied out (or a photocopy provided for each child) and the activity can begin. When all the rocks have been tested, make a chart of the results. It should then be possible to order the samples according to how much water each one can absorb. Finally, help the class

to reach and record a common conclusion. Encourage the children to think of the consequences of their conclusions and the uses of rocks that do not take up water. Introduce the word *permeability* and explain that this word describes the ability of a rock to let water soak in and pass through. A graph can be drawn to show the differences in permeability between the rocks tested.

Suggestion(s) for extension
Plan an investigation to find out how much water a piece of rock will take up. This will involve first weighing the rock, then soaking it in water overnight and weighing it again. Children should notice bubbles rising from the rock as air is forced out and the water takes its place. Different types of rock can be tried and compared.

Suggestion(s) for support
If necessary, the agreed instructions can be photocopied. As the whole class is involved in the investigation, children will be supported by each other's suggestions and ideas. Guidance with planning and recording will give confidence for tackling future investigational work.

Display ideas
The rocks can be arranged in order according to how much water they took up. Pictures of different landscapes will demonstrate the large-scale effects of water seeping through rocks. Provide different pieces of rock for individual children to test.

Other aspects of the Science PoS covered
Experimental and Investigative Science – 1a, b, c, d, e; 2a, b, c; 3a, b, c, d, e.

LOOKING CLOSELY AT SOILS

Soils are different from each other in their appearance and texture.

†† *Children working in pairs.*

🕐 *One hour.*

Previous skills/knowledge needed
Children will need to work successfully in pairs and be able to observe and describe in detail.

Preparation
Ask children to bring a small amount of soil from a garden they know, but have some spare samples ready as this may not always be possible. Also try to obtain amounts of clay and sandy soil with which to make comparisons. Keep the soils in lidded cartons.

Resources needed
Soil samples; hand-lenses; kitchen towels and newspaper; photocopiable sheets 122 (1 copy per child) and 123 (as required for support).

What to do
Tell the children that they are going to do a close examination of four soil samples. They will need to work carefully and scientifically. If they have already examined rock samples, they will already have ideas of what to look for. Encourage a careful description of the overall colour. Is it light or dark, patchy or the same all over? What can be seen with a hand-lens? Are the particles all the same? Are they of different sizes? Show the children how to test for texture by rubbing a pinch of soil between the fingers and deciding whether it feels gritty or smooth. Demonstrate how to find out whether the particles of their samples will stick together under pressure by placing a small amount in the palm of your hand and gently moulding it with the palm of the other hand to see if a ball is formed. Provide kitchen towels or newspaper to spread over tables before the investigation begins.

Use photocopiable sheet 122, which allows observations and results to be recorded from soil samples brought by two children as well as from two mystery samples provided by you. (One clay soil and one sandy soil.)

Finally, demonstrate how to do a soil smear by adding a small amount of water to a sample of soil and spreading a little of the mixture on to paper. The children can test each of their samples in this way and when they are dry, the colours the soils have left on the paper can be compared with each other. It might be advisable to do the soil smears on separate pieces of paper. They could be attached to the first column of the recording sheet or arranged on a separate sheet of paper.

Reveal to the children, if they have not yet discovered for themselves, that the mystery samples are clay and sandy soils. Which of these are the children's soil samples nearer to? It might be possible to draw a map, mark the sites from where the soils were taken and, depending on the locality, show useful information about the distribution of soil types.

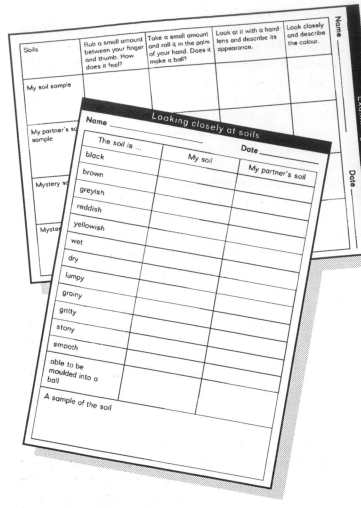

The soil is ...	My soil	My partner's soil
black	
brown	
greyish	
reddish	
yellowish	
wet	
dry	
lumpy	
grainy	
gritty	
stony	
smooth	
able to be moulded into a ball	
A sample of the soil	

Suggestion(s) for extension

To find out more about the constituents of a soil sample, put different soils in labelled jars and cover them generously with water. Stir or shake and leave for a few days to settle. Examine and compare the different layers which have formed – some soils will be shown to have uniformly-sized particles, while others will be seen to consist of a variety of different-sized particles. The amounts of decaying plant material which will collect on top of the samples can be compared.

Find out more about local soils.

Suggestion(s) for support

Provide a checklist to help with recording. Photocopiable sheet 123 can be completed using ticks, with the children comparing two soil samples and providing soil smears showing the colour to complete the page.

Assessment opportunities

Focus on the children's skills of observation and their ability to complete a chart successfully.

Display ideas

Arrange the soil samples and their corresponding smears together with appropriate vocabulary. Display a local map showing where the soils came from.

Other aspects of the Science PoS covered

Experimental and Investigative Science – 1c; 2b, c; 3a, b, c, e.

Reference to photocopiable sheets

Photocopiable sheet 122 provides a chart on which children can record their observations and soil smears. Sheet 123 allows children to record their observations of two soil samples using ticks, with space at the bottom of the page for soil smears (or for soil samples to be attached under a piece of clear adhesive plastic).

WATER DRAINING THROUGH SOILS

Water passes through soils at different rates.

†† *Children working in groups of three or four. If resources are limited, one demonstration could be observed by everyone. Ideally, the equipment should be set up early in the day for maximum observation.*

🕐 *45 minutes discussion and planning; 20–30 minutes to set up the test and make initial observations; experiment left overnight; ongoing observations and recording.*

Previous skills/knowledge needed

Children need to work co-operatively as a group and be aware of some of the stages involved in planning and carrying out an independent investigation. They also need to be able to record time efficiently.

Key background information

Water drains through soils at different rates. Clay soils are sticky when wet and become hard during dry spells; drainage is poor. Sandy soils do not hold water and drainage is rapid. An ideal soil for cultivation is somewhere between these two extremes. In this test, a measured amount of water is poured through a funnel containing a type of soil. The rate at which the water drains through is measured against a second and a third soil type.

Preparation

If necessary, collect identical plastic drinks bottles to make funnels. (Cut off and invert the top part of the bottle.) Obtain soil samples. Try out the test to determine the amount of soil and water that is best for the funnels being used.

Resources needed

For each group: three transparent containers, three large funnels, a container with a measuring scale in millilitres, kitchen towels, three soil samples (one clay, one sandy and one a random garden sample).

What to do

Explain to the children that you want them to find out what happens when rain falls on different soils. Listen to class suggestions as to how this might be done, and discuss problems and useful ideas. Then show the children the equipment you have collected and encourage them to work in their groups to find a way of using it to carry out the investigation. The degree of guidance needed will depend on the children's age, ability and previous experience in planning investigations, and it is important that they produce a detailed plan with a drawing of how they will set up the apparatus before the task is begun.

Three different soil samples are used for testing – one a clay soil, one a sandy soil and one which could be a local sample. The children should line each funnel with a piece of kitchen towel and then pack it with soil from one of the samples. They will need to use the same quantity of soil each time and pack as evenly as possible. Each funnel of soil is placed over a transparent container into which the water will drip. (See illustration below.)

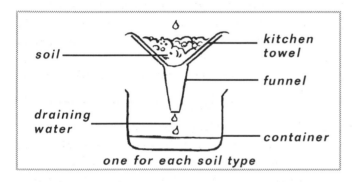

one for each soil type

The amount of water used will depend on the size of the funnel and the quantity of soil that is used. Each soil sample should receive the water at the same time so that comparisons can be made, but it might be necessary to add the water in stages if it cannot all be contained in the funnel. (If so, make sure this is done in all cases.) Try out the test beforehand so that you are familiar with the behaviour of the soils and the time the experiment will take. Children should be alerted to make observations from the moment they begin pouring in the water, but must also be prepared to wait in case the drainage is slow.

Helpful questions to ask during planning might include: What are we trying to find out? What do we think will happen? How will we carry out our plan? What equipment will we need? How will we make it a fair test? Why do we need to make sure the soil is packed evenly in each funnel? Is it important to use the same amount of water for each soil sample? Will anything need to be measured? In addition, ask the children what they will be looking for as evidence and encourage an efficient method of recording their findings.

If the experiment needs to be kept overnight, cover the soil with clingfilm to prevent any evaporation – especially if children decide to compare the amount of water poured into the soil with the amount that drains out.

When the children have their results, encourage comparisons between other groups and discuss any problems that might have arisen. Allow time for the children to describe what they did, what they observed and the conclusions they have reached. Allow time to repeat the test if this is considered necessary or useful. Reintroduce the terms *permeable* and *permeability*, and use them when comparing the different soils.

Suggestion(s) for extension

Let the children plant cress seeds in the three different types of soil to find out if there is any difference in the way the seedlings grow and develop.

Encourage the children to find out more about the drainage of local soils and how it affects farming methods.

Suggestion(s) for support

Some children may need more guidance with planning their investigation. Extra questions to ask might include: What will we need to keep the same in our tests? What will be different each time? What do you think will happen to the water? How will we know which soil drains better than the others?

Assessment opportunities

Observe children's ability to co-operate within a group, use equipment satisfactorily, make predictions and decide whether the evidence collected supports the predictions.

Opportunities for IT

Some children might like to record their work using a word processor or desktop publishing package. This would give them an opportunity to originate their work on the computer and to write in a different style. This activity could be offered to a small group of children over a longer period to give them opportunities to write at length using a word processor, with each group recording a different part of the science work. The accounts could be kept together in a class book.

This kind of writing requires children to record in a chronological sequence. The word processor will enable them to alter the order or add sections as they go and work and polish their writing to create an accurate account. In order to do this they may need to save and retrieve their work, learn how to 'cut and paste' or 'drag and drop' sections of text they wish to move. Some children may be introduced to the idea of *tabs* to create evenly-spaced columns for tables of results. Children should also be shown how to centre headings, add underlines and other simple text and format commands.

Older or more able children could even add pictures of their investigation which they have created with a graphics package, or drawn freehand and scanned into digital format using a hand scanner.

Display ideas

Create a display around the testing area featuring pictures of machinery designed to cope with heavy soils, and crops which are more suited to a particular soil type.

Other aspects of the Science PoS covered

Experimental and Investigative Science – all areas can be covered.

SOLID, LIQUID OR GAS?

Materials can be grouped into solids, liquids and gases.
†† *Children working together as a class and sharing ideas; discussing in pairs when appropriate.*
🕐 *One hour.*

Previous skills/knowledge needed

If children have been introduced to the idea that all materials are made up of tiny particles (molecules), they can more easily understand why solids, liquids and gases behave differently.

Key background information

Molecules in solid materials are tightly packed; they are attracted to each other by strong forces and do not move about, though they can vibrate. In a liquid the attraction is less strong, so the molecules can slide over each other. In a gas the attraction is weak, and molecules move freely and in a random fashion.

Resources needed

Photocopiable sheet 124 (as required); access to books for research and extension work.

What to do

Allow the children about ten minutes to list (individually) as many solids, liquids and gases they can think of. Suggest that they aim for ten in each list and tell them the time limit. At the end of this time, ask them which list was the hardest to compile; children may be unsure of what gases really are, and will probably not know the names of many gases at this stage. Take one category at a time and ask for examples, so that everyone can top up and extend their individual lists (which can be presented more neatly at a later stage). For many examples, children will agree straight away on the correct category; but there will be others of which they are unsure and where a decision cannot be made at this point. Encourage one child to act as scribe for the class and to record the uncertainties, which can be referred to and sorted later when more is understood about solids, liquids and gases.

During this activity, the children will be adding to their own ideas on the characteristics of solids, liquids and gases and the differences between them.

Next, allow a few minutes for discussion in pairs, so that the children can look at their lists and decide what is common to the examples in each group. How can they tell that a book, a piece of wood and a paper-clip are solids? What properties do milk, petrol and blood have in common as liquids? How would they describe a gas? Let them briefly write down their comments and then bring everyone together for a sharing of ideas, arriving at the conclusions that *solids* have a definite shape, do not move on their own and are quite easy to control; *liquids* have no definite shape, move easily and are more difficult to control; *gases* spread out in all directions and are the most difficult to control.

Explain that the molecules of which all materials are made up are grouped closely and in an orderly fashion in a solid; they are less regimented, more mobile and not so closely grouped in a liquid; and they are extremely mobile and unrestricted in a gas. (See illustration below.)

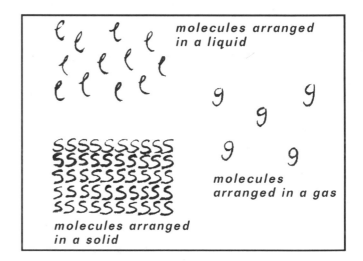

molecules arranged in a liquid

molecules arranged in a gas

molecules arranged in a solid

Children can record their lists and their discoveries about solids, liquids and gases. Encourage them to devise their own ways to record their findings.

Suggestion(s) for extension

Give pairs of children the opportunity to carry out their own research into liquids or gases. Suggest grouping substances according to whether they are harmful, helpful or essential.

Suggestion(s) for support

Provide pictures or lists of solids, liquids and gases which can be sorted by colour coding, symbols, or cutting out and rearranging. On photocopiable sheet 124, the individual pictures can be cut out for the children to sort; there is also the opportunity for children to provide some examples of their own.

Assessment opportunities

Photocopiable sheet 124 could be used as a simple assessment activity, to check that children can distinguish between solids, liquids and gases.

Opportunities for IT

Children could use an encyclopaedia CD-ROM to search for information on different types of gases and their uses.

Display ideas

Encourage children to create their own amusing display by depicting solids, liquids and gases as characters showing off their particular characteristics.

Other aspects of the Science PoS covered

Experimental and Investigative Science – 2b; 3a, b, e.

Reference to photocopiable sheets

Photocopiable sheet 124 has pictures and the names of items for children to identify as solids, liquids or gases. The marked corners can be colour-coded. This sheet can also be used for assessment purposes, or be adapted to make a game which the children can invent to test each other. There are spaces for children to add their own examples.

FLOW AND FALL

Liquids find their own level and take the shape of the container they are in.

†† *The class can work as a whole, with some children acting as demonstrators while the rest observe. Alternatively, a group situation could be organised to share the task; after recording their own observations, groups could move around the room to collect the rest of the information.*

🕐 *30–40 minutes.*

Previous skills/knowledge needed

Children should understand that the coloured water they are using represents the behaviour of the majority of liquids.

Key background information

Because of the behaviour of its molecules, a liquid will always move unless it is contained; and because of the force exerted by gravity, a liquid will always move to the lowest level it can find.

Resources needed

Food colouring; water; as many small containers as possible (such as a saucer, a drinking glass, a narrow transparent vase, a wide plate, bottles of different shapes and sizes); a plastic sheet or waterproof tabletop; a container with a measuring scale in millilitres; one large jug or several small ones. Transparent plastic tubing and funnels for the extension activity.

What to do

Depending on how the class is to be organised, arrange for a measured amount (100ml, several spoonfuls or an eggcupful) of the coloured water to be poured into the different containers. Tell the children that you want them to draw the shape of the liquid, but not the container. Pour the same amount of liquid on to a large, flat, plastic sheet to demonstrate the shapelessness of liquids.

Afterwards, where possible, suggest tilting the containers. Children can record their observations as drawings, this time including the outline of the container. Ask the children what they have noticed about the behaviour of the liquid. Is it possible to describe the shape of a liquid? What is a liquid always trying to do? Encourage the children to write a concluding sentence based on their observations of the behaviour of liquids.

Suggestion(s) for extension
Allow a group to investigate liquid levels with a length of transparent, flexible plastic tube, starting with a U-shape and pouring coloured water into one end using a funnel.

Assessment opportunities
Use individual children's concluding sentences to assess to what extent they have understood the behaviour of liquids.

Display ideas
Continue to collect unusually-shaped glassware, such as old vases, food jars and transparent plastic containers, to hold amounts of coloured water in order to emphasise the shapelessness of liquids.

Other aspects of the Science PoS covered
Experimental and Investigative Science – 2a, b, c; 3b, c, d, e.

DRIPS AND DROPS

Unlike solids and gases, liquids fall in drops.
†† *Children working in pairs.*
🕐 *10 minutes for instruction to the class; 30 minutes for the activity and recording.*

Previous skills/knowledge needed
Children will need to be aware that gravity pulls things towards the Earth's surface, which is why drops of a liquid fall downwards.

Key background information
The molecules of liquids in air or on a hard surface cling together to form drops. Although drops of liquids form at different rates according to the viscosity of the liquid, they all fall at the same rate because of the force of gravity. When drops of water meet an absorbent material, the molecules creep into the spaces between the fibres and the drop shapes disappear.

Preparation
Put small amounts of the liquids (see list below) into suitable containers so that there is enough for each pair to have a sample of each one. Practise making drops in order to show children the best technique to use.

Resources needed
Cooking oil, treacle, liquid honey, water and suitable containers to hold small amounts of these; tools to use for making drops, which could be pieces of straws, spoons or small droppers. Each liquid will need a tool of its own. Containers such as plastic dishes will be needed to catch the drips, and similar containers will be required in which to put the sticky equipment after use.

What to do
Give each pair of children the straws, droppers or spoons together with small amounts of water, treacle, liquid honey and cooking oil. Provide hand-lenses. Demonstrate how to collect very small quantities of each liquid with the tools, allowing a drip to form slowly and eventually drop into a suitable container. Encourage careful observations so that children can appreciate the shapes made, noticing the way the drops form and making comparisons between the behaviour of different liquids. Word pictures and drawings of the shapes of drops can be made. Explain that the liquid molecules cling to each other to form a drop, which is pulled downwards by gravity.

Suggestions for further investigation could arise from this activity. For example, children might want to know what happens to drops when they hit different surfaces.

Suggestion(s) for extension
Ask the children if it is possible to make drops of different sizes using different 'droppers', from those used before (a cocktail stick is a possible example), or by making different-sized holes in plastic bottles for the liquid to drip through. What is the smallest drop that can be made?

Compare the sizes of drops of different liquids. Instead of looking at one drop of each liquid, which could be difficult, try to make a pool of the same number of drops of each liquid and compare these.

Use water drops as lenses. Add a drop to a page from an old magazine to see whether it changes the appearance of the print. Experiment with different-sized drops and with drops on glass.

Suggestion(s) for support

It might be necessary for some children to practise using the tools to make drops before observations begin. Provide plenty of straws or spoons; wash droppers when necessary.

Assessment opportunities

Use the activity to assess children's ability to use equipment and organise an efficient test. Check their skills of observation.

Opportunities for IT

Children could use a video camera to record drops falling on to different surfaces. The recorded 'film' can then be replayed in slow motion and frames stopped at different points so that children can clearly see what happens to the drop. If the school has access to a digitiser these pictures can be fed into the computer and printed copies made for display of further work.

Display ideas

Prepare an area where children can continue to experiment with making drops. Arrange their drawings and descriptions to stimulate further discussion.

Other aspects of the Science PoS covered

Experimental and Investigative Science – 1a, b, c, d, e; 2a, b, c; 3a, c, d, e.

IT'S A GAS

Gases spread to fill spaces, therefore they are difficult to control.

†† *Whole-class discussion and demonstration, with individual recording.*

🕐 *20 minutes for discussion. 20 minutes for recording.*

Previous skills/knowledge needed

Most children will know that there is air all around them. If they understand that several different gases make up the atmosphere and are normally indistinguishable, they will begin to realise some of the difficulties which arise when dealing with gases.

Key background information

Air is made up of nitrogen (78%), oxygen (21%), carbon dioxide (0.03%) and other rare gases (0.97%).

Preparation

Make up a quantity of coloured water (enough to fill two-thirds of the bowl being used). If there is no tap in the room, make sure there is an example of a liquid which the children can locate at the appropriate moment (it could be a bottle of paint, water in a vase of flowers or a drink from someone's packed lunch).

Resources needed

Balloons; a small box; a transparent container; a bowl; food colouring.

What to do

Ask a member of the class to hand you any solid material they can find; ask another child to find a liquid, which will obviously have to be passed to you in some restricting container. Then ask for a quantity of gas. Encourage someone to make a list of the children's ideas of how to hand the gas to you – which could turn out to be quite amusing, but which will nevertheless prove that there are difficulties in controlling a gas. Have ready objects which will help to demonstrate the ideas as they arise, and which you can introduce into the discussion when appropriate. An 'empty' box will hold the gases of the atmosphere; a balloon can be blown up, trapping the air someone breathes out; and a transparent container, inverted over a bowl of coloured water, will show a pocket of trapped air.

Collect evidence of gases moving – there might be examples which can be seen through the classroom window, and the playground might be a good place to start. Examples might include branches and washing disturbed by the wind, paper blown by human breath, fumes leaving a chimney or car exhaust, shadows of steam moving, children feeling draughts or blasts of hot air on their hands and faces.

Recording could take the form of a page of evidence to

MATERIALS

show the presence of gases, perhaps with amusing illustrations of attempts to confine and contain a gas.

Take this opportunity to emphasise the dangers of some gases, such as household gases used for cookers or fires and emissions from cars.

Suggestion(s) for extension
Encourage children to find out more about the gases in the atmosphere, and what the weather forecasters mean by 'poor air quality'.

Find out how gases are contained and transported by people who use them, in factories, laboratories, hospitals, engineering works, and so on.

Suggestion(s) for support
Find diagrams and illustrations which show the presence and behaviour of gases, and which will help children to understand concepts that are not easy to demonstrate in the classroom.

Opportunities for IT
Different groups of children could use a CD-ROM encyclopaedia to search for information on different gases. The information could then be loaded into a word processor and edited to create a short information piece for display in the classroom. The teacher could ask different groups to search for different gases.

In order to do this, children will need to know how to save text from the CD-ROM and then reload it into their word processor. This procedure will differ depending on the computer, CD-ROM and word processor used. Once the text is loaded, children should edit it, by deleting unwanted

text, re-ordering the information and writing their own sections of text to link the ideas together. It would be a good idea to discuss with the class beforehand what kind of information will be needed, or possibly to allow them only 100 words so that they have to decide for themselves the most important information. This 'editorial' work could be done away from the computer using a highlighter pen on a printout of the text. Once the children have decided on the text they could return and retrieve their saved text to edit it and print it out for the display.

Display ideas
Display children's drawings together with pictures showing examples of gases being used. Write out the names of gases as children discover them in reference books, highlighting those which are dangerous.

Other aspects of the Science PoS covered
Experimental and Investigative Science – 2b; 3b.

WARMING AIR

As temperature increases, air expands and rises.

†† *Whole-class demonstration and discussion; children working on tasks individually or with the support of a partner.*

⏲ *30 minutes for demonstration and discussion; up to an hour for designing and making devices.*

Previous skills/knowledge needed
Children will need to know that air fills all the spaces around them, but its behaviour is difficult to observe as it is usually invisible.

Key background information
As air is heated the molecules become more active and tend to spread out further, which causes expansion. Density is reduced, so the warm air becomes lighter and rises above cold air. Helium is a gas which is lighter than air and is used to fill novelty balloons.

Resources needed
A balloon; a plastic bowl; card; lightweight types of paper and plastic; drawing materials; thread, string and scissors; a hair drier to supply hot air; pictures or a video of a hot air balloon; photocopiable sheet 125 (as required).

What to do
Demonstrate the expansion of air by resting a partly blown-up balloon (tied at the bottom) on the surface of a bowl of hot water. Ask the children what they notice. The balloon will appear to increase in size and then grow smaller again as the water cools. Ask for the children's ideas about why this

should happen. Explain that the air inside the skin of the balloon needed more space as it was warmed, and so pushed against the sides of the balloon as it tried to spread out. As cooling occurred, the air returned to its original volume still enclosed by the balloon skin. Ask the children what they think would have happened to the air if it had not been trapped inside the balloon. They will probably realise that it would have floated away. Explain that as the molecules spread out and air expands, it becomes lighter and rises.

Ask the children to tell you about hot air balloons. Someone might have been close enough to see one take off or land. Show pictures or a video of a hot air balloon and discuss what is happening when the air is heated and why the balloon rises.

Encourage the class to suggest where the air in the room might be moving; look for clues or set up indicators. There might be windows which open near the ceiling to let out the warm air; wisps of paper on displays above radiators might flutter; draughts might be felt. Ask the children to draw pictures showing examples of warmed air rising; explain that the routes the air takes are known as air currents and the currents can be represented by arrows.

Ask the children to design and make an air current indicator for a place in the school where they predict air is rising. The indicators should be made of lightweight material, and could range from simple streamers to more complicated spinning devices. Photocopiable sheet 125 provides instructions for creating a spiral snake which can be made to spin above a warm radiator. Several of these snakes could be hung around the room to detect areas where air movement is most vigorous.

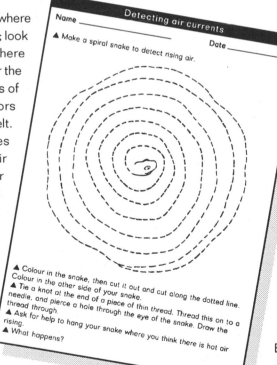

Detecting air currents

Name _____ Date _____

▲ Make a spiral snake to detect rising air.

▲ Colour in the snake, then cut it out and cut along the dotted line. Colour in the other side of your snake.
▲ Tie a knot at the end of a piece of thin thread. Thread this on to a needle, and pierce a hole through the eye of the snake. Draw the thread through.
▲ Ask for help to hang your snake where you think there is hot air rising.
▲ What happens?

Suggestion (s) for extension

Design and make a model of a hot air balloon. Start with a polythene bag or thin paper bag, or use tissue paper to form a rough balloon shape to hold the air. The balloon could be launched using a hair drier to heat the air below the balloon rather than to cause a strong current of hot air.

Find out why a helium-filled balloon always rises.

Research the development of airships and the movement of gliders.

Suggestion(s) for support

Use photocopiable sheet 125 if children need help with drawing a spiral.

Opportunities for IT

Children could use a CD-ROM encyclopaedia to research information on hot air balloons and gliding and then write short sections for an information display or small brochure.

Display ideas

The children's air current detectors will make an interesting display and can be supplemented with large arrows fastened to walls or furniture, demonstrating the movement of warmed air in that area.

Other aspects of the Science PoS covered

Experimental and Investigative Science – 1a, b , c, e; 2, b, c; 3b, c, d, e.

Reference to photocopiable sheet

Photocopiable sheet 125 offers instructions and an outline of a spiral snake which can be used if children have difficulty with drawing when making their air movement detector.

BUBBLES

Gases can be seen as bubbles when contained within liquid.

†† *Whole-class demonstration and discussion, followed by observations in groups of 4 or 5.*

🕑 *One hour.*

Previous knowledge/skills needed

Children should have formed some ideas about the behaviour of gases and be able to make careful observations and recordings.

Key background information

Bubbles are small amounts of gas temporarily trapped, usually within a liquid.

Preparation

Make up a mixture of washing-up liquid and water and practise blowing bubbles using a loop made from a piece of wire, to make sure the solution is effective.

Resources needed

Washing-up liquid; thin wire; a large bottle of clear fizzy drink; a handful of lentils, sultanas or raisins; drinking straws; a glass or jar for each group; photocopiable sheet 126 (one copy per child).

What to do

Demonstrate bubble-blowing or arrange a bubble-blowing competition between you and the class. Use a loop of wire and a concentrated mixture of water and washing-up liquid.

Ask the class what they think a bubble is. Write all the useful suggestions on the board, until everyone realises that inside a bubble there is a small volume of trapped gas. Explain that in this case, the liquid has stretched around a small amount of air from your breath and trapped it for a short time.

Ask for other examples of bubbles the children have seen; suggestions will probably include bubbles in fizzy drinks, in fish tanks, in the bath and when food is cooking. Children can record their observations of bubbles on the first part of photocopiable sheet 126.

Ask the children to produce bubbles by blowing into water through a straw. Where has the gas come from and where does it go to? Next, produce a large bottle of a clear fizzy drink and ask the children what will happen when the cap is released. Discuss the behaviour of the bubbles in the liquid, but do not open the bottle just yet. Explain that the bubbles are pumped into the drink as it is made in the factory, and that the gas is pure carbon dioxide. Ask how long the children think the drink will take to lose its fizz once the bottle has been opened.

Divide the class into groups of four or five. Tell the children that each group will be given a glass of the drink and they must closely observe the behaviour of the bubbles. You will also be giving them a sultana each to drop into the drink, as this will help with their observations. Pour out the drink into glasses and give one to each group. Ask the children to write down all their observations on photocopiable sheet x. They will notice that bubbles attach themselves to a sultana, carrying it to the surface; as the bubbles burst, the sultana sinks collecting more bubbles on the way down, and eventually rises to the surface again. Rising and sinking will occur until all the bubbles have escaped from the drink and it has become flat. Ask the children why the bubbles do not remain in the liquid; discuss why they rise to the surface, and what happens to them there. Where does the gas go to when the bubbles burst? How will the children know when the drink is flat (without tasting it)?

Bubbles

Name

Date

Bubbles are

▲ Draw the bubbles in these pictures. The last two are for your own examples.

▲ Draw your glass of fizzy drink.

The bubbles in the fizzy drink are

▲ Describe what is happening to the bubbles in the drink.

▲ Why do the bubbles rise to the surface?

▲ What has happened when the drink has gone flat?

▲ How long did it take for the glass of fizzy drink to lose all its bubbles?

Suggestion(s) for extension

Find out how much carbon dioxide there is in a can of fizzy drink by weighing the can, opening it to release the gas and weighing it again the next day when it will have gone flat. Leave it in a cool place or refrigerator to minimise the evaporation.

Suggest that the children compare two or more fizzy drinks to see which one keeps its fizz the longest.

Use books to find out what the gas is inside the bubbles that come from the bottom of a pond.

Suggestion(s) for support

Write down the children's observations on the appropriate parts of the recording sheet to assess their understanding of the behaviour of gases.

Opportunities for IT

Children could use a graphics package to draw large bubbles into which they then type their bubble information for display purposes. Similar results could be achieved using a word processor with children using the 'centre' command to arrange their text in a bubble shape. The bubble shape itself could be drawn by hand after the work has been printed out.

Display ideas

Use large decorative bubble shapes on which the children can write scientific facts that they have discovered about bubbles from their observations.

Other aspects of the Science PoS covered

Experimental and Investigative Science – 2b; 3b, c, e.

Reference to photocopiable sheet

Photocopiable sheet 126 asks children to record their experience of bubbles together with their observations and conclusions related to the activity.

MAKING AND COLLECTING GASES

Gases are produced when some materials are mixed together.

†† *Whole-class introduction and instruction, followed by children working in pairs.*

🕐 *One hour.*

⚠ *Care should be taken when handling some of the substances in this experiment.*

Previous skills/knowledge needed

Children should be aware that due to their properties, gases are difficult to contain and most of them are difficult to see.

Key background information

Vinegar and lemon juice are acids. Each one reacts with bicarbonate of soda to produce the gas carbon dioxide.

Preparation

Test the fizzy sweets available (see below).

Resources needed

Sherbet tablets or other fizzy sweets are ideal; balloons; test tubes or narrow-necked bottles; bicarbonate of soda; washing soda; citric acid crystals; vinegar or lemon juice; dried yeast and sugar.

What to do

Begin by giving each pair of children a narrow container with a small amount of water in it (a test tube is ideal) and a fizzy sweet. Ask the children to add the sweet to the water and then take it in turns to put a thumb over the end of the tube, at the same time observing carefully. Discuss what has happened. Explain that a gas is produced which can be seen as bubbles in the water. It can also be heard and felt, but not easily captured.

Tell the children that when some materials are mixed together, there is a reaction and a gas is made. Ask for suggestions as to how the gas could be collected. Be prepared to try out any workable idea and explain that one way to collect any gas produced is by attaching the mouth of a balloon over the neck of the container, as soon as the materials are mixed together, thus preventing any gas escaping into the atmosphere.

Before beginning the experiment, give each pair of children a bottle and balloon, so that they can practise fitting the two together.

Now explain the test. Tell the children that they will be given two materials to mix together in the container, and that they should then observe the reaction and collect any gas which is produced. If each pair of children is doing only one test, use different mixtures for different pairs so that comparisons can be made. Explain that the liquid should be put in the container first and the solid material added to it. A paper funnel will prevent the solid material (powder) from being spilt. The balloon will need to be attached as quickly as possible and careful observations made. Suggest that the children share the task, with one adding the solid material and the other fixing the balloon, but both observing. Allow the children time to discuss and record their plan before starting. They will need to explain how they are going to make the gas and how it is to be collected. A drawing of the collecting method should be included.

When this is done, the test can proceed. The children should record the materials tested and the results themselves and describe what happened. If sufficient equipment is available, each pair can carry out further tests, otherwise information will have to be exchanged with other groups which have tested different materials.

Other reactions that the children could try include: bicarbonate of soda and warm water; bicarbonate of soda and vinegar; bicarbonate of soda and lemon juice; washing soda and vinegar; citric acid crystals and water; a mixture of dried yeast, sugar and warm water. Most reactions occur immediately. However, the yeast mixture needs a warm spot, the gas takes longer to be produced, and the balloon will gradually increase in size.

Bring the children back together to discuss their results. In what ways were the reactions similar? Which materials were the most reactive when mixed together? Discuss the use of bicarbonate of soda in baking when it is used to make cakes rise, and the purpose of yeast in bread-making. Point out that the holes in cakes and bread were made by the trapped bubbles.

Suggestion(s) for extension

Let the children prepare some cake mixture, noting the texture before and after cooking. If half the mixture is made with bicarbonate of soda and half without, the difference made by the gas bubbles should be easily recognised.

Make some bread rolls with and without yeast, to demonstrate the importance of yeast in making the dough rise.

Suggestion(s) for support

Children who have difficulty with recording sheet can show what happened in a drawing and symbol form.

Display ideas

Set up the yeast experiment in various places around the room for children to compare the amounts of gas produced. Create an information board showing how gases are used to help make the things we eat and drink.

Other aspects of the Science PoS covered

Experimental and Investigative Science – 1a, b, c; 2a, b, c; 3a, b, c, e.

Changing materials

This section aims to extend children's experiences of heating, cooling, dissolving, melting, boiling, condensing, freezing, evaporating and burning. The activities are designed to show how different materials are affected by these processes, and to indicate whether the changes which occur are reversible or irreversible.

Children are made aware of the importance of these processes in our everyday lives – whether they happen naturally, as evaporation and condensation do occur in the water cycle and freezing and melting occur during winter, or are brought about for particular purposes such as sweetening drinks (dissolving), making pots (baking) or drying clothes (evaporation).

A range of tasks enables children to explore and investigate the processes which cause materials to change. They provide opportunities for asking relevant questions, making predictions and observing closely. Children are encouraged to share ideas and work co-operatively. They will learn how to plan and record their work scientifically, and how to draw conclusions.

MIXING MATERIALS

When materials are mixed, changes can occur.

†† *Children working in groups of four to test between four and eight materials.*

🕐 *15–20 minutes for preliminary planning; 30–40 minutes for testing and recording; 15 minutes for reporting back.*

Previous skills/knowledge needed

Children will need to be able to work purposefully in a group and use equipment efficiently. They will need to understand what is meant by 'mixing' and 'changing'.

Key background information

Many materials react when mixed together, causing changes to occur. Mixing safe, everyday materials with water will demonstrate reactions and changes that children can observe. The bicarbonate of soda mixture will give off a gas; salt will dissolve; cooking oil will not mix with the water but will form a layer on the surface; food colouring will dye the water and custard powder and cornflour will cause the liquid to thicken and behave as a viscous liquid, which can be moulded into a ball with quick finger movements and then become a liquid again; heat is produced when water is mixed with plaster of Paris. If test-tubes are used, the following quantities are appropriate: approximately 10ml of water each time, half a teaspoon of salt, one teaspoon of bicarbonate of soda, soil and cooking oil, a few drops of food colouring. Put a heaped teaspoon of cornflour onto a saucer, add one teaspoon of water and stir carefully. Add more water if necessary. With plaster of Paris, follow the instructions given and use according to the size of the container chosen for mixing.

Preparation

Collect together the equipment you are going to use and put small amounts of the substances into labelled jars – provide enough for each group to have at least four materials to test. Write out an instruction list to give guidance on the amount of each material the children should use.

Resources needed

A quantity of small transparent containers (the groups will need one container for every material they test). The plaster of Paris is best mixed in a shallow disposable container and the cornflour in a saucer. If test-tubes are available, only small amounts of the liquids and other materials need to be used; larger containers will need larger amounts to make the reactions more easily observable. Materials for testing can include salt, food colouring, cooking oil, plaster of Paris, bicarbonate of soda, custard powder, cornflour, soil. Hand-lenses, spoons, containers with a measuring scale in millilitres and a kitchen towel. Each group will also need a plastic jug or other water container.

What to do

Explain to the class that each group will be given several named materials to which they are going to add water and then stir or shake, if necessary. (The written instructions you give them will advise on the quantities and the type of container they should use.) They must observe closely, listen and record what happens. They will also need to devise a suitable framework for recording their results.

Distribute spoons, jars containing the materials (but not the water), hand-lenses, containers with a measuring scale in millilitres, other containers for mixing. Allow 15 to 20 minutes for the groups to familiarise themselves with the task and to devise and record an efficient working plan. Only when each group can convince you that it is prepared should the jug of cold water be provided and testing allowed to begin.

Ask the children to record their plan and to describe each material before it is mixed with water – they should note its

appearance, including colour and texture. As they perform each test, encourage the children to make detailed observations and comments. Where children need help with this part of the activity, questions to ask might include: Did anything happen immediately after the materials were mixed together? Did the materials mix together easily? Was there a change in colour? Can you still see both materials? If there were bubbles, what might be happening? Does the water and cornflour mixture behave like a liquid or a solid? What happened after you left the mixtures to stand for a while? Children should be encouraged to keep checking their mixtures at intervals, as the reaction with the plaster of Paris will not be instant. Point out that they can record what they see (and possibly hear or feel).

When all testing is complete, each group can report in turn and compare their results with other groups. Ask how many different changes have been observed.

Suggestion(s) for extension
Demonstrate that there is a change in density when salt is added to water. Make a hydrometer by covering one end of a piece of drinking straw with a small lump of Plasticine (see Figure 1). Float the hydrometer (closed end downwards) in tap water and then in salt water. The hydrometer will float higher in the salt water, which is denser than the tap water. Also try floating an egg first in tap water, then in salt water. What can be observed?

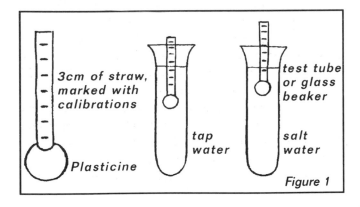

3cm of straw, marked with calibrations

Plasticine

tap water

test tube or glass beaker

salt water

Figure 1

Suggestion(s) for support
The children will support each other while carrying out the testing by asking questions and sharing observations. Provide opportunities for repeating any test they would like to try again. A bank of words or symbols on display for the whole class can help with recording. Key words will include the names of the materials and equipment being used and words which describe what is taking place, such as measuring, mixing, pouring, stirring, disappearing (or dissolving if children understand this term), bubbling, heating.

Assessment opportunities
Focus on individual children's ability to follow instructions and work efficiently, and to observe and record successfully.

Opportunities for IT
Each pair of children could word-process a description of what happened when one of their materials was mixed with water. These could be printed out and used as part of a class display or for a class booklet about mixing materials.

Display ideas
Collect picture examples and ask the children to draw their own illustrations of 'changes' which are not possible to observe in the classroom, such as industrial processes, chemicals mixed together to make plastics or glass, and so on.

Other aspects of the Science PoS covered
Experimental and Investigative Science – 1c; 2a, c; 3a, b, c, e.

HEATING SOLID MATERIALS (1)

Heating some solid materials causes changes which can be reversed by cooling.

†† *Groups of four or five arranged around a table so that everyone can safely see what is happening in the bowl of hot water, as well as having space for recording.*

🕐 *30 minutes for initial planning; 30 minutes for activity and recording; 10 minutes for discussion.*

⚠ *Care is needed when dealing with hot substances.*

Previous skills/knowledge needed
Children will need to be able to understand that heat passes from a warmer material to a cooler one, and be able to discuss and work as a group. The ability to use a stopwatch and thermometer will allow the task to be extended.

Key background information
As a material becomes warmer the molecules vibrate more rapidly; the molecules of some solid materials begin to move about more freely, and the material becomes a liquid. The temperature at which this happens varies according to the material of which the solid is made.

Resources needed
A supply of hot water, small pieces of materials such as chocolate, margarine, lard, solid jelly, banana, bread, cheese, ice, wax crayon, candle (all roughly the same size); paper-clips and plastic buttons or counters; small foil dishes (cake containers are ideal); plastic bowls to hold hot water; photocopiable sheet 127.

What to do
Tell the children that they are going to heat certain materials and look for any changes that take place. The heat supply

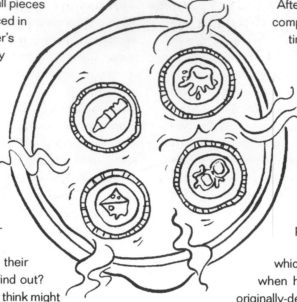

will be hot water in a bowl, and small pieces of the various materials will be placed in foil dishes to be floated on the water's surface. Ask the children what they expect will happen, what problems might arise and how they will make sure they carry out the test safely. Point out that if comparisons are to be made between the different materials, each one will have to be placed upon the water at the same moment. Encourage the group to organise this part of the test co-operatively.

Now ask the children to record their planning. What are they trying to find out? How will they do this? What do they think might happen? How will they make sure the experiment is safe? The children will also need to fill in the chart on photocopiable sheet 127, on which they can draw and list the materials they are testing as well as describing their appearance and texture before they are heated.

Encourage the children to think of questions they might need to answer as the test proceeds. These could include: Which material is the first to show any change? What sort of changes are taking place? Do any of the materials change their colour? Which materials show only a small change? Which materials do not change at all? Which material is most affected by the heat? What happens to the materials as the water cools? When the children have sorted out their planning and recording, the test can begin. Supply the water as hot as is safely possible. The children's observations and comments as the test is in progress can be made as rough notes or written directly on to photocopiable sheet 127.

After all testing is complete, discuss and compare the results as a class and allow time for photocopiable sheet 127 to be completed.

Suggestion(s) for extension

Questions arising from the test could lead to further investigations. For example: how could the melting process be speeded up? Children might suggest breaking the materials into smaller pieces or using a more powerful source of heat.

Use moulds to show the shapes which chocolate can be made to take when heated, and make Easter eggs or originally-designed sweets. Show the children how to write their names on greaseproof paper with a thin trickle of melted chocolate. Chocolate can be used to decorate cakes made in the following activity.

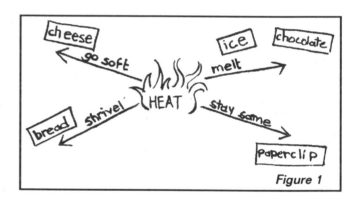

Figure 1

Suggestion(s) for support

Photocopiable sheet 127 offers support for recording. The names of the materials being tested, as well as other key words, can be displayed as a word bank.

Display ideas

Make a large visual flow chart with a representation of a heat source at the centre. Draw arrows emanating from the heat source and write the words 'melt', 'shrivel', 'go soft' and 'stay the same' along them (see Figure 1). Children can draw or write the name of each material they have tested on to card and pin these at the point of the appropriate arrow.

Other aspects of the Science PoS covered

Experimental and Investigative Science – 1b, c; 2a, b; 3a, b, c, d, e.

Reference to photocopiable sheets

Photocopiable sheet 127 provides a chart to include observations.

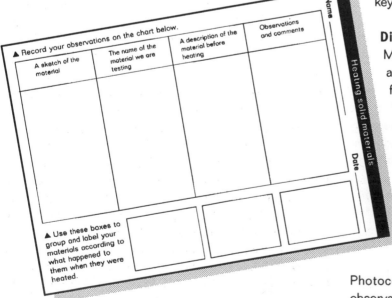

HEATING SOLID MATERIALS (2)

Heating some materials can cause changes which cannot be reversed by cooling.

†† *As children will need very close supervision, it might only be possible to demonstrate one activity at a time. Where parents or classroom assistants are available, groups of children can each perform a different task and share their results with the rest of the class. It should be possible for every child to be directly involved in some stage of an activity.*

⏱ *Time needed for preparation and cooking will determine how long is needed for these activities.*

⚠ *Bear in mind any dietary restrictions if the food is to be eaten. Children should follow appropriate safety procedures where heat is being used, and should be aware of hygiene considerations (see below).*

Previous skills/knowledge needed

Children will need to be aware of the dangers when working with high temperatures and hot equipment, and understand the need for appropriate safety measures. They should be aware of the importance of hygiene: washing their hands before and after handling food, keeping hair tied back where necessary and avoiding coughing and sneezing when close to food.

Key background information

Many cooking processes require high temperatures which change the nature of the food being cooked. Usually these processes cannot be reversed. Suggestions for cooking activities which can be attempted in the classroom include: baking potatoes, making cakes using a cake mix, boiling eggs. Dough can be made and baked, not for eating but for model-making.

Preparation

Decide which activities can most easily be undertaken, depending on availability of equipment and classroom help. Prepare equipment and food for chosen activities; check any electrical equipment and organise the areas for working. Make sure that appropriate safety measures are taken and water and cleaning materials are available.

Resources needed

Access to a conventional oven, microwave or boiling ring; cooking equipment including baking trays, cake tins, mixing bowls, wooden spoons, saucepans, aluminium foil; washing-up facilities; the chosen ingredients (such as potatoes, eggs, cake mixes); plain flour, salt, cooking oil; craft boards or suitable working surfaces for modelling; aprons or other protective clothing.

What to do

Explain to the children that they will be cooking different types of food by baking or boiling them. They will be helping as much as possible with the preparation, so they will be able to examine the foods before cooking and again afterwards.

▲ *Baked potatoes*: Wash and scrub the potatoes, pierce with a fork and wrap in foil if a conventional oven is being used. Ask the children: Do the potatoes feel hard or soft as they are being washed? Is it easy to pierce the potato with a fork? After baking, show the children how you can test to see if the potatoes are cooked by using a fork or skewer. Then divide the potato into portions for sampling. Slice an uncooked potato so that the change which has taken place can easily be seen. Ask the children what the differences are between the uncooked and the cooked potato.

▲ *Cakes*: Show the children the cake mix and any other ingredients you have decided to use. Ask them to describe their colour and texture. Point out that the ingredients would be rather unpleasant to eat in their present state. Follow the instructions given on the packet to prepare the mixture. Ask what changes have already taken place. After baking, the cakes can be tested by eating and the children can describe the changes that have taken place during the cooking process. Do the children think the process could be reversed?

▲ *Boiled eggs*: Crack an egg into a saucer so that the children can examine it closely and understand that this is how it looks before heating. Boil the eggs for at least five minutes. When cool they can be shelled and divided to eat with bread and butter or crisps. (*Make sure that eggs are well cooked before eating.*) Discuss what effects the boiling has had on the eggs. Ask if the eggs could be returned to their original state.

▲ *Dough models*: Children can make up a quantity of dough to be used not for eating but for making models, which can be baked hard and then painted. Two children can mix ten heaped tablespoonfuls of plain flour with a teaspoonful of salt; four teaspoonfuls of cooking oil are then added, and gradually about eight tablespoonfuls of warm water as the dough is mixed. Encourage the children to describe the dough as they squeeze and stretch it. More flour can be added if the mixture gets too sticky. When an even consistency has been achieved, the modelling can begin. Encourage the children to sketch their models before they are baked. After

MATERIALS

baking and cooling, the models can be examined again and changes noted. Point out that it is not possible to reclaim the original ingredients: the changes which happen during heating are irreversible.

Children's recordings of these activities can take the form of 'before and after' drawings accompanied by observations and comments.

Suggestion for extension

If several cooking activities can take place, a party can be organised. A pancake party is also an enjoyable way of demonstrating the effect of heat (via heated oil) on a mixture of flour, milk and eggs.

Suggestion(s) for support

Give oral instructions as children proceed with a task, guiding and helping with use of equipment where necessary. Ask for the assistance of parents and other adults.

Display ideas

Display recipes, the children's 'before and after' drawings and their models. Photographs of children preparing and enjoying the food will remind them of the processes involved.

Other aspects of the Science PoS covered

Experimental and Investigative Science – 1e; 2a, b; 3b, c, e.

BELOW ZERO

Cooling materials can cause them to change.

†† *Ideally, children could work in groups; but as each group will require space in a freezer, this might not be possible. If this is the case, a whole-class demonstration could be more practical, with everyone contributing to the planning and experimental elements.*

🕐 *30–40 minutes for discussion, recording and setting up the test; 20–30 minutes on the following day for collecting and recording the results.*

Previous skills/knowledge needed

If children have explored the heating, melting, cooling and solidifying of chocolate, wax, lard (or solid vegetable fat) and other materials, they will have some understanding of the way in which lowering the temperature can change these materials back from a liquid to their normally solid state. In this activity, the effects of cooling below the freezing point are investigated.

Key background information

As materials are cooled, their molecules move and vibrate less. Materials which normally exist as a liquid take on a solid form. The temperature at which this happens varies according to the material involved.

Resources needed

Polythene bags; materials to freeze, such as water, chocolate, soil, washing-up liquid, butter, lard (or solid vegetable fat), bread, a paper-clip, a plastic cube, a pebble, a pencil, a piece of soap; photocopiable sheet 128 (one copy per child). A coolbox will be useful.

What to do

Explain to the children that they are going to investigate the effects of cooling on some materials. They will be making the materials as cold as possible so a freezer must be used. If there is a really cold spell with freezing temperatures, the materials can be tested outside.

Show the children the materials to be used and ask for their predictions of what will happen. Which will freeze? Which will not be affected? Ask the children how they will decide if freezing has occurred.

Examine and discuss the appearance and texture of each material before freezing. This information can be recorded on photocopiable sheet 128 together with the children's planning details. Fasten each material loosely inside a polythene bag. The materials will need several hours in the freezer and are probably best left overnight. Encourage the children to examine the cooled materials quickly on removal before any further changes occur. If a cool box is available, the materials can be examined one at a time while the others are kept cold. If freezing has taken place outside, the materials can be examined outside. Ask a pair or group of children to observe the stage of each material and then report back to the class. The information can be discussed by the whole class, with children making individual recordings on photocopiable sheet 128.

Questions to prompt the children's observations might include: Has the material changed its shape or colour? How does it feel? Does it look any different after freezing?

Finally, encourage the children to group the materials. Possible groupings might be: those not at all affected; those which have changed from a liquid to a solid; and those which have become harder. Leave the materials on display as they thaw out, so that the children can see that the changes which occurred as a result of cooling can be reversed.

Suggestion(s) for extension

Find out about liquid nitrogen, which is used by doctors and scientists. Materials unaffected by temperatures just below the freezing point of water become brittle and can easily break when immersed in liquid nitrogen. This is a very rapid way of freezing materials.

Suggestion(s) for support

Help those children who find it difficult to reach a conclusion about how the materials have changed. Provide samples of the materials at normal temperatures, so that comparisons are easier to make.

Assessment opportunities

Assess individual children's ability to predict and make decisions based on observations.

Display ideas

Arrange samples of the materials to compare with those that have been frozen. Label appropriately.

Other aspects of the Science PoS covered

Experimental and Investigative Science – 1b, c; 2a, b; 3b, c, d, e.

Reference to photocopiable sheets

Photocopiable sheet 128 provides a framework for planning the investigations and a chart for individual recording of the results.

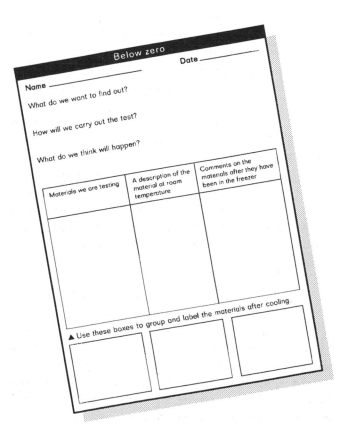

FEELING HOT, FEELING COLD

Temperature is a measure of how hot or cold things are.

†† *Whole-class introductory session, followed by children working in small groups and reporting back to the whole class.*

⊙ *15 minutes for introduction, about 30 minutes for group task (depending on number of locations to visit), 20–30 minutes for discussion and recording.*

Previous skills/knowledge needed

Children's precise understanding of the terms hot, warm, cool and cold will vary according to age and experience.

Key background information

One person's perception of how hot or cold something feels is not necessarily the same as another's, and communicating this information in a scientific way is not possible. Therefore there is a need for an accurate instrument to measure temperature.

Preparation

Draw a plan of the school with enough information on it for the children to find their way about as a simple orienteering exercise. Decide and mark locations on the plan where children can safely assess the temperature (some should be places where the temperature is fairly obvious, while others should require more thought). Photocopy the plan so that each child in the class has a copy.

Resources needed

Photocopies of the simple plan of the school (one for each child), photocopiable sheet 129 (one copy for each child as required); clipboard; books for reference.

What to do

Provide each child with a plan of the school and a clipboard. Explain that they will be touring the school and stopping at certain locations marked on their plan, to decide whether the temperature is hot, warm, cool or cold. Decide on a method of representing these terms, either by colour coding or by symbols. Make a key to show this.

Allow the children to work in groups; each group does not necessarily have to cover all locations, but there should be enough information collected for comparisons to be made.

When all the groups return, consider their results. Encourage them to record the temperatures in their locations using the four categories: hot, warm, cool, cold. Discuss whether it was easy or difficult to make decisions within the group, what the problems were and whether the different groups generally agree.

Introduce the word 'temperature' and check that the children understand what is meant by this word. Talk about the scientific need for some way of measuring temperatures, measuring the changing of temperatures and communicating these sets of measurements.

Suggestion(s) for extension

Provide three bowls of water for the children to test – one fairly hot, one warm, and one cold with added ice cubes. Ask them to put one hand in the 'hot' bowl and one in the 'cold' bowl. After about a minute, carefully remove both hands and put both in the warm bowl. This will demonstrate how we can be tricked into estimating temperature inaccurately, and is a further example of the need for a common method of measuring how hot or cold something is.

Suggestion(s) for support

Children who require further help in understanding the distinction between the terms 'hot', 'warm', 'cool' and 'cold' can use photocopiable sheet 129. The pictures can also be cut out and arranged in sequence.

Feeling hot, feeling cold

Name _____   Date _____

▲ These words describe different temperatures. Look at the pictures below. Decide which description is the best for each picture. Write the words in the spaces below each picture.

very hot   hot   warm   cool   cold   very cold

Display ideas

Children can collect pictures or provide drawings of different situations demonstrating hot and cold, warm and cool, and group these to make a collage.

Othe aspects of the Science PoS covered

Experimental and Investigative Science – 1c; 2b; 3b, c, e.

Reference to photocopiable sheet

Photocopiable sheet 129 asks children to match pictures with the appropriate words, describing a variety of different temperature situations.

USING THERMOMETERS

The instrument used to measure temperature is a thermometer.

†† *Whole-class introduction, then children working in pairs with thermometers if enough are available; activity and recording done individually.*

🕐 *20 minutes for introduction and handling thermometers; one hour for activity and recording.*

Previous skills/knowledge needed

Children will need to understand that temperature is a measure of how hot or cold things are. To make a model thermometer they will need to be able to use scissors accurately.

Key background information

There are different types of thermometers; some indicate temperature by expansion of liquids (coloured spirit or mercury), some by a dial which operates through the expansion and contraction of a metal coil, some electronically and others by the effect of temperature on liquid crystals. There are some thermometers with sensitive probes for measuring hot liquids or soil temperatures. Digital and liquid crystal display thermometers are the easiest for younger children to read.

Preparation

Collect and check thermometers before use.

Resources needed

Thermometers of different types including domestic, scientific, clinical, LCD, digital, incubator and freezer thermometers; photocopiable sheet 130 (one for each child); scissors, adhesive and crayons.

What to do

Show the class a thermometer – if possible, one the children are already familiar with, such as a room thermometer or one from the class science resources. Check that everyone knows what it measures. Explain that temperature is measured in small units called degrees Celsius, and that the temperatures they are most likely to encounter range between 0 and 100 degrees.

Briefly describe what the thermometer is made of, and explain that it is a delicate piece of equipment that needs to be handled carefully. Point out the liquid inside, and explain that it rises and falls in the glass tube as it expands and contracts, thus indicating the temperature. Allow each child to handle a thermometer of this type, and observe the movement of the liquid as they hold the base or bulb part in their hands. Explain that this is due to the heat from their hand travelling to the liquid in the bulb. This is a good time to point out that when reading a thermometer, fingers should not touch the bulb area and the reading should be taken with the eyes level with the point the liquid has reached. Ask the children to check the room temperature, which is the temperature of the air, and to compare this with the temperature the thermometer shows when their hand is holding the bulb.

Use photocopiable sheet 130 to make a model of a thermometer which the children can operate to help them understand how a real thermometer works.

Suggestion(s) for extension

Look at different types of thermometers; find out their range of measurement and the job they are intended for.

LCD room temperature monitors are sometimes available from Energy Management bodies. Use these, or other thermometers, to check the temperatures of areas around school and compare them to recommended temperatures. 18°C is a recommended classroom temperature and 16°C a recommended corridor temperature.

Take regular temperature readings, record these on charts and use the information to plot graphs.

Suggestion(s) for support

Give assistance if children have difficulty in reading the scale of a thermometer. Cut the appropriate parts for children needing help when making their model thermometer.

Assessment opportunities

Ask individual children to tell you the temperature of the classroom or other areas of the school each day, in order to check that they can read a thermometer correctly.

Opportunities for IT

It is often possible to set up the computer as a thermometer by linking a thermistor to the computer through an interface and with appropriate software. An alternative is to use a hand-held temperature probe which will record the results of readings over a period of time. These can then be downloaded on to the class computer and graphs can be drawn of the results.

Display ideas

Arrange a variety of thermometers around the room so that children can become familiar with the different types. Display specialist thermometers with labels explaining where and how they are used. Make a giant thermometer representation on which the usual room temperature can be marked.

Other aspects of the Science PoS covered

Experimental and Investigative Science – 1e; 2a, b, c; 3a, b.

Reference to photocopiable sheets

Photocopiable sheet 130 can be used to make a simple model of a thermometer out of a single sheet of A4 paper. The children can use this to familiarise themselves with the working of a real thermometer. Children can carry out the instructions themselves or the whole class together can follow the instructions step by step with help from the teacher.

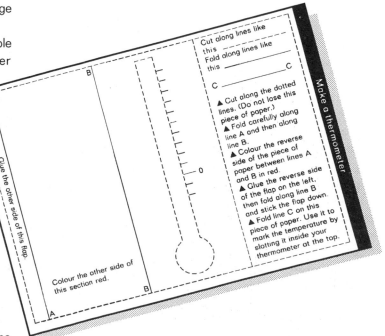

LOOKING AT COLD TEMPERATURES

Cold temperatures can be measured.

†† *Whole-class discussion, followed by children working in pairs; individual recording. Allow time for research.*

🕐 *20 minutes for leading up to activity; 30 minutes for activity and collecting information; 30 minutes for research if needed.*

Previous skills/knowledge needed

Children will need to have had experience of handling and using a scientific thermometer.

Key background information

By using ice in a transparent container, children will be able to see the liquid in the thermometer shrink to show a temperature close to 0°C. The temperature inside a refrigerator will register between 1°C and 7°C, and that inside a freezer compartment between –2°C and –23°C.

The lowezst natural temperature recorded on Earth is –89°C (in Antarctica). Scientists think that the lowest temperature which could be reached anywhere is –273°C, known as Absolute Zero.

Preparation

Make ice-cubes.

Resources needed

Scientific thermometers; a freezer thermometer if possible; small transparent containers; ice cubes; photocopiable sheet 131. Salt is needed for an extension activity.

What to do

Ask the children to think of the place with the lowest temperature they could measure. Where might it occur? Suggestions might include outdoor winter temperatures and the temperature of a refrigerator or a freezer. Ask for ways in which they could record a really low temperature in the classroom. Suggestions might include checking the temperature of the water from the cold tap or using ice.

Give the children the opportunity of estimating these temperatures – their accuracy will depend on their knowledge and understanding of freezing temperatures and their experience of using minus numbers. Discuss what happens to water at a low temperature and make sure that the children understand that this happens at 0°C. Explain how temperatures below freezing are recorded.

Allow all of the children's ideas to be checked and the temperatures recorded, from the highest to the lowest. That of freshly drawn tap water is easily measured; a scientific thermometer can be put in a fridge for half an hour; a special thermometer able to record low temperatures will be needed for a freezer. Meanwhile, working in pairs, the children can use a thermometer to see how low a temperature they can obtain with ice-cubes or crushed ice in a small transparent container. Use photocopiable sheet 131, which encourages children to order these low temperatures.

Suggestion(s) for extension

Investigate the effect on the temperature of ice if salt is added.

Ask the children to carry out a 'low temperature search' to find examples of very low temperatures, such as daily newspaper weather reports from around the world, interesting scientific data sent from Antarctic bases, or conditions in space discovered by astronomers.

Suggestion(s) for support

Draw a large number scale which extends from –10°C to 10°C, so that children can become familiar with using minus numbers.

Assessment opportunities

Observe individual children to see if they can read temperatures below freezing point on a thermometer independently.

Opportunities for IT

An interesting activity in this topic is to use a temperature probe placed in a refrigerator and linked to a computer. The graph which is drawn on the computer screen will enable children to see what happens to the temperature inside the fridge when the door is opened and closed. The thermometer could be moved to different shelves and differences noted. This could lead to an interesting discussion on the best part of the fridge in which to store different foods.

The use of the temperature probe linked to the computer is a good way to introduce line graphs to children. The software can be set up to record the temperature every minute and, as it is recorded, the next point in the line graph is plotted. This visual display helps children to link the opening of the door to changes in temperature.

Display ideas

Add relevant interesting 'minus' temperatures to a large wall representation of a thermometer. Create a 'cold temperature zone' in the classroom, featuring pictures of and facts about freezing temperatures conditions.

MATERIALS

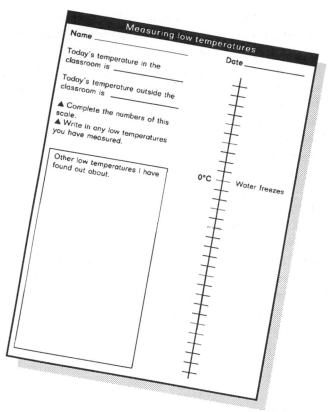

Other aspects of the Science PoS covered
Experimental and Investigative Science – 1e; 2a, b, c; 3a, b.

Reference to photocopiable sheet
Photocopiable sheet 131 provides a temperature scale on which children can mark low temperatures and include other information they have collected.

LOOKING AT HOT TEMPERATURES

Hot temperatures can be measured.
†† *Whole-class discussion, followed by children working in pairs; further class or group discussion and opportunity for research.*

Previous skills/knowledge needed
Children will need to have had experience of handling and using a scientific thermometer.

Key background information
It is not safe for children to measure temperatures approaching boiling point, though they might have noticed temperature scales on ovens or other cooking equipment. High temperatures the children might find interesting include the temperature of the Universe immediately after the Big Bang (which is estimated at 10^{39} degrees Celcius), the highest temperature obtained in a laboratory (10^8 degrees),

the temperature on the surface of the Sun (7000 degrees) and the melting point of tungsten (3140 degrees). Compare these with the temperatures in Britain during a heatwave (usually around 30°C).

Preparation
Check the thermometers before use.

Resources needed
Scientific spirit thermometers; fever strip LCD monitors; books for research.

What to do
Ask the children to think about the highest temperatures they could measure safely – they will probably suggest the water from the hot tap, the air near a radiator, outside on a really hot day, or even themselves. Give the children the opportunity of estimating these temperatures before measuring them. If children are going to check their own temperatures, fever strip monitors should be used.

Find out if the children understand what happens to water at 100°C, and discuss extremely high temperatures which can only be calculated by scientists (as there is no thermometer which could do the task). Provide the opportunity for children to research and collect information about very high temperatures. Children could order the measurements and information they find in boxes or lists for recording purposes, as a single scale would be difficult to devise with such immense numbers involved.

Suggestion(s) for extension
Encourage children to research how astronomers measure the temperatures of stars (it is the colour of the star which indicates its temperature).
From newspapers, cut out daily weather reports from around the world; the children can locate the hot spots on a map and make graphs of high temperatures over a month.

Suggestion(s) for support

Assist with the reading of thermometer scales where this is necessary. Make an enlargement of any scale which is small and difficult to read, and use this to demonstrate readings.

Assessment opportunities

Continue to ask individual children to check daily temperatures, in order for you to assess their skill in recording a thermometer.

Opportunities for IT

Children could use a CD-ROM encyclopaedia to research information about hot temperatures. They could also use a simple graphing package to plot graphs of different temperatures around the world taken from daily newspapers. If children use a spreadsheet to record these temperatures, the results can be collected and displayed over several days, or even weeks. The statistical functions of the spreadsheet can be used to give average temperatures, to identify the hottest and coldest days in any one place and to plot graphs of the changes of temperature over time. With some spreadsheets it is also possible to plot several graphs on the same axis – this would allow direct graphical comparisons to be made between temperatures in different parts of the world.

If children have access to electronic mail through the Internet or other systems such as COMPUSERVE, they may be able to find out about weather in other parts of the world not shown in newspapers.

The spreadsheet could be set up like this:

	a	b	c	d	e
1	**Date**	**School**	**London**	**Cairo**	**New York**
2	1.9.95	15			
3	2.9.95	14			
4	3.9.95	17			
5	4.9.95	15			
		ave (b2:b5)	ave (c2:c5)	ave (d2:d5)	

Children could also use a temperature probe linked to the computer to record the changes in temperature in the classroom during the day. If the probe can be placed outside, the changes in external temperature can also be recorded. In very cold weather children may be interested to notice what happens if the probe is placed below the surface of the soil. Does it stay warmer and get colder below the ground? Does the depth make any difference?

Display ideas

Include relevant and interesting high temperatures on a large wall representation of a thermometer. Create a 'hot temperature zone' in the classroom, with appropriate pictures and facts.

Other aspects of the Science PoS covered

Experimental and Investigative Science – 1e; 2a, b, c; 3a, b, e.

FREEZING AND MELTING

Freezing and melting are changes which can be reversed in many materials.

✠ *If freezing facilities are limited, groups will need to work at different times. Experiments will need to be set up on one day and observations made the next, with plenty of time for the children to handle and examine their ice shapes.*

🕐 *After a brief introductory discussion, children will need up to 30 minutes to organise and record their ideas. For the second session, up to an hour will be needed for observations and recording.*

Previous skills/knowledge needed

As this is an exploratory activity, children need to observe carefully and make notes scientifically.

Key background information

Water and ice are the obvious materials for demonstrating the cycle of freezing and melting; other materials also undergo the freezing and melting processes, but at different temperatures.

Preparation

Quantities of ice are required and access to a freezer or the freezing compartment of a refrigerator is essential. Ice cubes can be stored in a vacuum flask until needed.

Resources needed

A freezing facility; a variety of small plastic containers; larger trays or bowls in which to hold the melting shapes while observations are taking place; food colouring; hand-lenses; ice cubes; a vacuum flask.

What to do

In winter, freezing temperatures present opportunities for exploring various forms of ice. Encourage the children to use hand-lenses to examine ice ferns on windows, frozen dew

Changing materials

on plants, icicles and ice on puddles. Point out that this is water in the environment that has turned to ice as the temperature has dropped.

Children can devise their own experiments to leave outside overnight. They can test different amounts of water, or find out if hot water cools and then freezes in the same way as colder water. Suggest that the children bring their tests to the classroom the following day to observe the melting process. Take this opportunity to warn of the dangers of ice on ponds. Allow plenty of time for observing and handling ice shapes.

At other times the use of a freezer will be necessary. Depending on the freezing space available, encourage children to use a variety of plastic containers to make their ice shapes. Egg cups, plastic cups, tubes, dishes and polythene bags (securely tied) will all allow interesting observations to be made. Suggest that children make drawings of the liquid in the containers before freezing and, if possible, make some measurement of the volume of the water used. As the ice shapes are examined after freezing, encourage the children to compare the volume of the shapes with that of the water used, to look for patterns within the ice, to consider the shape of the frozen ice and to observe melting. It is useful if annotated drawings and notes of observations are made as a record. Make sure the children are aware of the freezing – melting – freezing cycle which is taking place, and that this is a reversible change.

Suggestion(s) for extension

Find out about the different uses of ice including ice in sport, ice for building igloos, ice for eating, ice for preserving foods, ice for sculpture, ice for first aid and preserving medical supplies. Make ice-cream or ice lollies.

Discover the purpose of ice houses, which were used before refrigeration was invented.

Suggestion(s) for support

Provide a simple classroom demonstration using a small quantity of water, which can be frozen to produce ice and allowed to melt again.

Assessment opportunities

While the children are examining their ice shapes, talk to individuals to assess their understanding of the cycle of freezing and melting.

Opportunities for IT

If children become interested in snowflakes as a result of this work they might like to design their own snowflake patterns using a suitable art or graphics package. They could begin by researching types of snowflake patterns, possibly drafting a design on paper before transferring it on to the computer.

This work would give children opportunities to use some of the more sophisticated drawing and design commands such as 'copy', 'flip' and 'rotate'. The children should only draw one segment of the snowflake, then use the copy or duplicate commands to make the other five segments, rotating and moving them into the correct places to make the complete snowflake. If the software has a 'snap to grid' facility, this will help the children to align the various segments when fitting them together.

Display ideas

Make a display of the drawings of ice shapes and highlight appropriate vocabulary. Arrange pictures of water and ice in their different forms and emphasise the melting and freezing processes.

Other aspects of the Science PoS covered

Experimental and Investigative Science – 1b; 2b, c; 3c, e.

MATERIALS

DISSOLVING

When a solid material dissolves in a liquid, a change has occurred.

†† *Teacher demonstration to the whole class.*

🕐 *30 minutes.*

Previous skills/knowledge needed
Children's knowledge of dissolving will depend on their individual experiences of stirring sugar into drinks and perhaps using salt in cooking.

Key background information
As a material dissolves in a liquid, it separates into its component molecules which spread among the molecules of the liquid and cannot be seen. Although the liquid might still look the same, its properties could be very different.

Preparation
Collect containers, such as two drinking glasses, and make sure that they are completely clean. Make a hydrometer to compare the density of tap water with that of salt water, by plugging one end of a drinking straw with a small ball of Plasticine.

Resources needed
A transparent jug or similar container; two smaller transparent containers; a quantity of salt; a drinking straw and Plasticine; an egg if required.

What to do
Demonstrate the process of dissolving to the whole class, using a transparent container of clean water and a quantity of salt. Ask the children to describe the water and the salt before mixing, and get them to record their observations.

Pour the same amount of water into two identical containers and into one stir a quantity of salt. Ask the children what has happened. There is no need to use the words 'soluble' and 'solution' at this stage. Everyone should notice that the salt has disappeared. Explain that the tiny particles of which each salt grain is made up have spread out amongst the particles of water and so cannot be seen by our eyes, though they are still there. Compare the liquids in the two containers – could the children say which is which if the containers were swapped round while they were not looking?

To help with identification and to prove that a change has happened and that the liquid is now different, allow a taste test. (Take this opportunity to explain that tasting should only be done with a teacher's permission, and is allowed this time because edible substances have been used and everything has been kept very clean.) It is also possible to show that dissolving salt in the water has made it easier for things to float in the new liquid by demonstrating the different levels at which a hydrometer, or an egg, will float in the two liquids.

Record the differences between the two liquids and together with the children, devise and record a statement to define dissolving.

Suggestion(s) for extension
Dissolve other soluble materials, for example sugar.

Suggestion(s) for support
Assist with recording and give extra help if needed to form a statement to explain dissolving.

Assessment opportunity
Observe individual children's understanding of dissolving through discussion and by checking their recording sheets.

Display ideas
Include work on dissolving in a display demonstrating processes which are reversible.

Other aspects of the Science PoS covered
Experimental and Investigative Science – 2b; 3b, e.

EVAPORATION

Evaporation is a natural process.

†† *Whole-class discussion and brainstorming session, both inside and outside the classroom, followed by a whole-class activity or children working in small groups.*

🕐 *30–40 minutes outdoor observation, depending on weather conditions and examples available; 30 minutes for activity and recording.*

Previous skills/knowledge needed
Children's experience of evaporation will vary; the first part of this section provides a basis from which to develop further the children's understanding of the process.

Key background information
Molecules with sufficient energy can escape from the surface of a liquid into the air. As the temperature rises, more molecules gain energy, and the rate of evaporation increases. Molecules of water evaporate to form water vapour. Energy can come from the sun, or a direct heat source such as a radiator or human skin.

66

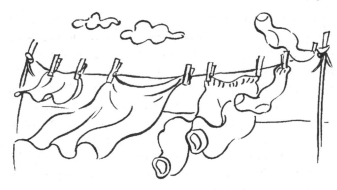

Preparation
Try to be flexible with planning and select a suitable day to collect outside examples of evaporation.

Resources needed
Kitchen cloths; a large transparent tank for holding water; chalk; two shallow containers; photocopiable sheet 132.

What to do
If possible, choose a day when evaporation is evident due to the weather conditions. Take the children outside and look for evidence of evaporation, which could include puddles drying up, tarmac steaming in the sun after a heavy summer storm, baked earth, a lower water level on a pond, washing drying on a line. Indoor examples of evaporation might include water spilled on the floor, a tabletop which has been wiped over with a wet cloth, a wet towel on a radiator, a painting drying after an art lesson. Discuss what is happening to the water and explain that when a liquid becomes a vapour or a gas, we say that it has evaporated.

Point out examples of evaporation occurring all around. Children could draw round a puddle with chalk at intervals on a dry day to record its shrinking; or during a dry spell, they could mark the water level of a pond or bowl of water left outside. Experiments in the classroom might include: wiping a surface with a wet cloth and watching the pattern of drying; leaving a piece of bread on a plate and checking its condition after a day; marking the water levels on the side of an open transparent tank of water over several days.

The children can record their evidence of evaporation occurring indoors and outdoors using words and pictures.

Ask the children if they can think of anything which might affect the rate at which evaporation occurs. They will know that clothes dry more quickly on a windy day and that ponds gradually dry up in hot weather. To show that rising temperature increases the rate of evaporation, groups of children can put a container of water in a warm place in the classroom, such as above a radiator or on a sunny window-sill. A second container can be left in a cooler spot. Ask the children what they think will happen. What other factors will need to be kept the same to make this a fair test? Which factor will be different for the two containers? For recording purposes, photocopiable sheet 132 can be used.

Suggestion(s) for extension
Encourage a group of children to set up a test to compare the rate at which water evaporates from different-shaped containers, such as a tray, a bottle, a cup and a small bucket.

As an investigation, ask a group of children to find out where evaporation is occurring at the fastest rate around school. Children could be asked where the best drying spot in school is on a particular day, or whether evaporation is faster indoors or outdoors.

Collect samples of how the process of evaporation has been used in food production, including dried fruits, dried peas and beans, dried fish, and evaporated milk.

Suggestion(s) for support
Provide a word bank in which the word 'evaporate' is written clearly together with other key words children might need when recording their examples.

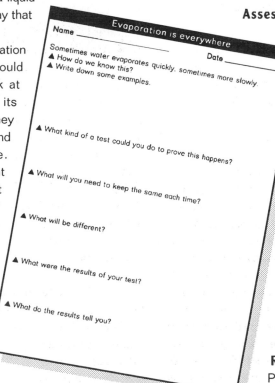

Assessment opportunities
Talk with children to assess how well they understand the process of evaporation.

Display
Where possible display collected evidence of evaporation or children's work demonstrating the process. Provide containers in a variety of shapes, each holding the same amount of water, so that the rates of evaporation can be observed daily.

Other aspects of the Science PoS covered
Experimental and Investigative Science – 1b, c, d, e; 2a, b, c; 3b, c, e.

Reference to photocopiable sheet
Photocopiable sheet 132 provides a framework for recording.

EVAPORATION FROM DIFFERENT LIQUIDS

Different liquids evaporate at different rates.

†† *An experiment for groups or the whole class, depending on equipment and space available.*

🕐 *30–45 minutes for planning, recording and setting up the test; opportunities on the following days for observation. If possible, arrange that the test is started on a Monday so that there are four days for observation. Finally, allow 20 minutes for communicating findings and evaluating.*

Previous skills/knowledge needed

Children need to know what is meant by evaporation, and to have seen and discussed evidence of it taking place (see the 'Evaporation' activity).

Key background information

Children's experience of evaporation will mainly involve water becoming water vapour and perhaps fumes rising from petrol. Most liquids which can be tested safely will be water-based. Children should be aware that liquids other than water also evaporate, at different rates (pure alcohol and fluids used in dry cleaning are examples of liquids that evaporate much more rapidly than water).

Preparation

A safe flat area, where the tests can easily be observed but will not be disturbed, will be needed. Collect liquids to test.

Resouces needed

Saucers are ideal for this activity, as the rate of evaporation can most easily be seen. Groups will need a saucer for every liquid being tested. If the number of saucers or the space is limited, each group can take responsibility for a different liquid or the whole class can work as a unit observing one set of liquids. Possible liquids to test include: water, vinegar, cooking oil, different drinks, and possibly perfume. A container with a measuring scale in millilitres and photocopiable sheet 133 (one per child) are also needed.

What to do

Tell the children that you want them to investigate whether one liquid evaporates more quickly than another. Ask for suggestions as to which liquids could be used safely. Three or four different liquids can easily be compared. Next, ask what type of container would be most suitable to hold the liquids. A shallow dish or saucer shows the rate of evaporation most clearly. The children might suggest putting the containers of liquids in a warm spot to speed up the process, making observations at regular intervals. Discuss the importance of fair testing. Ask which factors will need to be kept the same – the containers must be identical and placed close together to receive the same conditions, and the amounts of liquids should be carefully measured out.

Encourage the children to make a chart to collect their results from daily observations. Use photocopiable sheet 133, if necessary, for this purpose – children can write in the appropriate dates (Day 1 will be the first day after the test was set up). Allow the groups to organise their test, labelling the saucers, and provide five to ten minutes on each of the following days for observations to be recorded. Finally bring together the whole class to discuss the observations and comments which have been made. Did one liquid appear to evaporate more quickly than the others? Order the liquids according to rate of evaporation. Did the test remain fair throughout? Explain that evaporation rates are considerably greater in other liquids, such as petrol and cleaning fluids, which for reasons of safety cannot be used in the classroom.

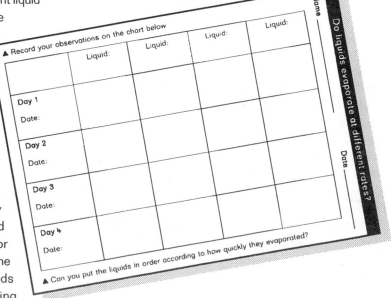

Do liquids evaporate at different rates?

Name _____ Date _____

▲ Record your observations on the chart below

	Liquid:	Liquid:	Liquid:	Liquid:
Day 1 Date:				
Day 2 Date:				
Day 3 Date:				
Day 4 Date:				

▲ Can you put the liquids in order according to how quickly they evaporated?

Suggestion(s) for extension

Ask children to find out more about the evaporation of liquids it is not possible to test in a classroom. They could research industrial processes which use evaporation. (Again warn them not to experiment with unsafe liquids at home.)

Suggestion(s) for support

Further help with planning might be necessary, especially when making sure that the test is fair.

Assessment opportunities

During the testing and recording, assess individual children's concepts of a 'fair test'. Suggest using more of one liquid than another, using different containers, or having different positions for each container, and listen to the children's comments.

Display ideas

Create a large representation of the molecules of a liquid escaping into the air to give a visual model of the evaporation process. Make the test itself into a display, including recording cards for the daily observations.

Other aspects of the Science PoS covered

Experimental and Investigative Science – 1a, b, c, d, e; 2a, b, c; 3a, b, c, d, e.

Reference to photocopiable sheets

Photocopiable sheet 133 provides a framework for recording observations.

MIXING MYSTERY MATERIALS

Dissolving and evaporating are changes which can be reversed.

†† *Some children will enjoy doing this task individually; others will prefer the support of a partner, either to help with interpreting the instructions or to assist with the task itself.*

🕐 *30–40 minutes for organising the test and recording; a day's wait for evaporation to take place; 20 minutes to complete observations and recording.*

Previous skills/knowledge needed

Children will need some understanding of the processes of dissolving and evaporation.

Key background information

This task combines the processes of dissolving and evaporating, and demonstrates that a dissolved material can be recovered by evaporation. The water will become part of the atmosphere and, in this task, will not be available for recovering. Many soluble materials form interesting crystals as a solution dries up; this happens because the molecules arrange themselves in a regular pattern as evaporation occurs. Stains can sometimes be noticed when water has evaporated and left behind the materials which were dissolved in it. Washing and rinsing dissolves the materials again and so they seem to disappear.

Preparation

Measure samples of soluble materials into the dishes for each child or pair. Use a variety of materials, but at this stage do not tell the children what they have. Collect other equipment. Reserve a safe flat area for observation of the evaporation process.

Resources needed

For each child or pair: a hand-lens; a small dish; a container of water; a spoon; a plain saucer; labelling equipment. Soluble materials: salt; sugar; bath salts; citric acid crystals; Epsom salts; washing soda. Photocopiable sheets 134 (one per pair) and 135 (one per child).

What to do

Tell the children they are going to carry out a task using step-by-step instructions. These can be presented in written form or as a set of pictures, given orally by the teacher, or read out by another child. The instructions are given on photocopiable sheet 134. Provide each child or pair with a dish containing a small amount of an unknown soluble material (identified by a code), a small container of water, a spoon and a plain saucer or flat dish, as well as labelling equipment, a hand-lens, a copy of the instructions and (for each child) a recording sheet.

Allow the children as much independence as possible during this task. Explain that you would like them to work from the instructions, discussing and organising the task with their partner, with as little extra help from you as possible, and recording their progress on photocopiable sheet 135. This will give them the opportunity to make their own decisions and to work responsibly and co-operatively, as well as increasing their confidence. Step in where problems arise, if help is needed with interpreting the instructions, if disputes arise, or if guidance is needed with recording.

As evaporation takes place, children will see crystals forming and can compare and match their samples with others. When the class has decided how many different materials were used and has perhaps been able to identify some of them, you can reveal what they were. Discuss the formation of crystals. Talk about any problems the children encountered.

Suggestion(s) for extension
Evaporate liquids to find out what might have been dissolved in them. Try tap water, rain water, sea water, stream water, cola. Hard water will have more minerals dissolved in it than soft water.

Find out why the Dead Sea is so salty and how salt is recovered for our use.

Encourage children to think about stains left by liquids. Look for those around a stainless steel sink where the water has dried; try removing stains on clothes or fabrics, comparing the effectiveness of cold water and hot water. Plan an investigation to find the best way of removing food stains from babies' bibs.

Certain other chemicals will produce interesting crystals but must only be used under strict supervision; these include copper sulphate, ferrous sulphate and chrome alum.

Suggestion(s) for support
Redraft, read out or use illustrated instructions where necessary. Children will support each other by working in pairs and sharing skills. As children should be familiar with the processes involved, encourage independent working and

give help only where it is needed for the test to proceed. A visual representation of the cycle of dissolving and evaporating can be displayed, and children can refer to this for extra support.

Assessment opportunities
Focus on individual children's ability to follow instructions, work co-operatively and in a scientific manner and record efficiently.

Display ideas
The evaporating liquids should be conveniently displayed for continual observation; labels with key words should be arranged nearby for children to refer to when discussing and recording. Display pictures of crystals of different materials.

Other aspects of the Science PoS covered
Experimental and Investigative Science – 1b, c; 2a, b; 3c, e.

Reference to photocopiable sheets
Photocopiable sheet 134 gives the children step-by-step instructions to carry out the task. Sheet 135 is a recording sheet to be used in conjunction with the instructions.

CONDENSATION

Cooling causes condensation.

†† *Whole-class discussion, then children working individually.*

🕐 *45 minutes.*

Previous skills/knowledge needed
Children should have some understanding of the behaviour of gases, and be aware of the process of evaporation. (See previous activities.)

Key background information
Condensation occurs when a gas turns back into a liquid because of a fall in temperature. The most common experience of this is when water vapour in the air is cooled and condensation forms on windows.

people's breath can be seen condensing as it meets the cold air. Use photocopiable sheet 136 to record examples of condensation.

To demonstrate other examples of condensation, put several items (such as a mirror, a glass, a ceramic cup, a plastic cup and a wooden spoon) inside a fridge for a few minutes. Meanwhile, ask the children to predict and record what might happen to each item as it is removed from the cold environment. Which items do they think will cause condensation to occur?

Suggestion(s) for extension
Investigate the formation of dew and frost.

Find out about other gases condensing, particularly in industrial processes.

Find out how a cooling tower at a power station works.

Suggestion(s) for support
Write out the key words 'condense', 'condensing' and 'condensation', along with 'warm' and 'cold', 'gas' and 'water vapour'; then use arrows and these words to make a visual demonstration of the links in the condensation process.

Assessment opportunities
Talk to individual children and use photocopiable sheet 136 to assess their understanding of the process of condensation.

Display ideas
Encourage the children to help set up a condensation collector for the class to observe. This could take the form of a shallow dish or tray of water over which a piece of clear polythene is fixed (either diagonally like a sail, domed, or tent-shaped). Make sure that the water which condenses can drip from the polythene into a collecting container. Leave the apparatus to stand in a sunny spot or over a radiator.

Preparation
Access to a refrigerator is required.

Resources needed
Mirrors; hand-lenses; photocopiable sheet 136 (one copy per child).

What to do
Look for and provide examples of condensation as a starting-point for comment and discussion. Ask the children to blow on their hands. Does their breath feel warm or cold? Then ask them to place their hands on a mirror or window pane (both should be glass). Does the surface feel hot or cold? Point out that they have proved to themselves that breath is warm and a mirror surface is cool. Then, when the mirrors have cooled again, tell the children to breathe directly on to them.

Explain that *condensation* is the name of the process whereby the water vapour in the air is turned back into a liquid due to cooler temperatures. Encourage the children to think of other cold surfaces where they have observed condensation. Classroom windows can often become 'steamed' up; bathroom mirrors and tiles cause condensation. Severe condensation in homes can bring problems which some children might have experienced. People who wear glasses could tell of the difficulties they experience on entering a warm room, or when removing hot food from an oven. On a very cold day,

Other aspects of the Science PoS covered
Experimental and Investigative Science – 1b, c; 2a, b; 3a, b, c, d, e.

Reference to photocopiable sheet
Photocopiable sheet 136 provides an opportunity for children to record their observations of everyday condensation, and offers a chart for their predictions and the results of the activity.

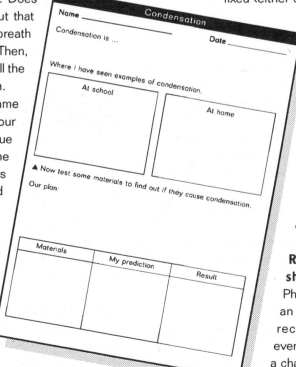

BOILING AND CONDENSING

Evaporation and condensation are changes which can be reversed.

♦♦ *Teacher demonstration to the whole class.*

🕐 *20 minutes for demonstration and discussion; 30 minutes for recording.*

⚠ *During the teacher demonstration, make sure everyone is safely seated and well away from the boiling kettle.*

Previous skill/knowledge needed

Children should be aware that the boiling liquids they are likely to encounter are very dangerous and can cause serious burns. They must understand that safety measures are extremely important where there are hot liquids involved.

Key background information

As water heats, the molecules become more and more mobile, eventually escaping from the surface and into the air. When water begins to boil, the molecules escape as steam. For an instant they are invisible, but soon form to water vapour (small droplets) as they meet the cooler air.

Preparation

Set up the experiment safely before beginning.

Resources needed

A kettle; photocopiable sheet 137 (one copy for each child).

What to do

Ask the children what they can tell you about boiling. They might already know that water boils at 100° Celsius; that it is important in cooking; that steam is produced; and that boiling liquids are dangerous and can scald. Ask the children what they can tell you about condensing. The information can be recorded on photocopiable sheet 137.

Demonstrate the boiling of water using a kettle. Carefully direct the steam towards a cold surface such as a window

to show condensation occurring. Discuss the possibility of recovering the condensed water. Ask the children for their own ideas about how to collect the drips and trickles of water as it runs down the cold surface. They might suggest directing the steam on to a cold surface such as a plate or metal tray, from which the water can drip into a collector. A plastic sheet can also be manipulated to direct the water into a container. Emphasise the cycle of water heating → water boiling → steam condensing back to water again.

Boil some more water, this time a small amount in a saucepan; and allow children to observe safely the 'splashy' movement of the water. Put a lid on the saucepan and ask the children to think what difference this will make. Will condensation still occur? What will happen to the quantity of water?

Ask for suggestions as to how you could find out how much water has been lost during boiling. Children will probably suggest measuring the amount of water before boiling and again afterwards when it has cooled.

Collect examples of situations where boiling is useful to us. Children can record their knowledge and observations of boiling on photocopiable sheet 137.

Suggestion(s) for extension

Encourage the children to find out about boiling water at high altitudes and the problems encountered by mountaineers and explorers.

Suggestion(s) for support

Some children might need help to compose their replies to the questions on the recording sheet. Steam can be described using a diagram, with arrows; sketches can be drawn to demonstrate the movement of steam from saucepans if children find this concept difficult to understand.

Assessment opportunities

Use the children's recording on photocopiable sheet 137 as well as discussion to check their understanding of the processes of boiling and condensation.

Opportunities for IT

Children could use a word processor or desktop publishing package to write their own labels to be used as part of a display on the cycle of boiling. The elements of the display could describe what is happening at different points in the cycle. Children could be given an opportunity to try using different fonts and sizes to create a label that is readable from a distance.

Display ideas

Create a visual demonstration of the cycle of boiling.

Other aspects of the Science PoS covered

Experimental and Investigative Science – 2b.

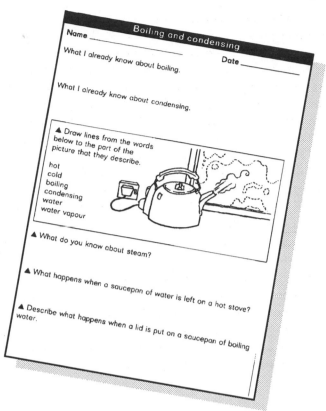

Boiling and condensing

Name _____

Date _____

What I already know about boiling.

What I already know about condensing.

▲ Draw lines from the words below to the part of the picture that they describe.

hot
cold
boiling
condensing
water
water vapour

▲ What do you know about steam?

▲ What happens when a saucepan of water is left on a hot stove?

▲ Describe what happens when a lid is put on a saucepan of boiling water.

Reference to photocopiable sheet

Photocopiable sheet 137 encourages children to record their observations and understanding of the cycle of boiling and condensing.

 THE WATER CYCLE

Evaporation and condensation are natural processes in the water cycle.

†† *Whole-class introduction, followed by children working in pairs.*

🕐 *10 minutes for introduction; 30–40 minutes for activity.*

Previous skills/knowledge needed

Children will need to have explored the processes of evaporation and condensation (see previous activities).

Key background information

The simplest representation of the water cycle is that rain falls on land and drains into the sea; evaporation occurs and water vapour rises into the air; when cooler air is reached, the water vapour condenses into tiny droplets of water which form clouds; the droplets get bigger and heavier until they fall as rain. However, water can evaporate from any exposed body of water, fall over both land and sea, and be part of many other processes before evaporation occurs. Water used by humans will probably be processed by a water treatment works in the course of its journey.

Preparation

Collect appropriate books and contact the local water authority to obtain any available information.

Resources needed

Reference books and water authority information; photocopiable sheets 138 (one copy per child), 139 (one copy per child) and 140 (as required); scissors and adhesive.

What to do

If possible, choose a rainy day and ask the children to write down any of the things which could happen to the rainwater falling on their home, school and local area. The possibilities are many, and children can be encouraged to draw tracking maps to show this:

falls on my house roof → runs down drainpipe → into the drains;

falls on our garden → soaks into the ground → taken up by roots of a cherry tree;

falls on playground → evaporates → becomes water vapour → forms clouds → falls as rain again.

Using their existing knowledge, reference books and resources available from water authorities, pairs of children can see how far they can follow their first ideas on how the water cycle works, including the terms *evaporation* and *condensation* where appropriate. Photocopiable sheet 138 provides suggestions which can be cut out and arranged on a large sheet of paper, with the children drawing in arrows to connect the stages and highlighting the words *evaporation* and *condensation*. This will help children to begin to realise that the water all around them – the rain, water in ponds, on the playground, from their taps – is all passing through a stage in the water cycle and if they could trace and study just one raindrop, they would find it was continually evaporating and condensing.

To clarify their concept of the processes involved, give the children sheet 139, which is a representation of the water cycle. Discuss the features shown in the picture and ask the children what is happening. Make sure that they can read the words at the bottom and understand what they mean.

Tell them to try to fit the words into the places on the picture where they think they belong. Arrows can also be drawn to show the direction of movement within the cycle.

Suggestion(s) for extension

Encourage children to find out about the drainage of water in the local area – where the nearest brook is, which stream or river it flows into and where the river reaches the sea.

Contact the nearest water treatment works and arrange a visit for the class.

Consider the importance of clean water, how pollutants might get into the cycle, and how they can be removed.

Suggestion(s) for support

Photocopiable sheet 140 explains the water cycle very simply and helps children to locate where the processes of evaporation and condensation occur.

Assessment opportunities

Photocopiable sheet 140 asks children to order the processes of the water cycle and can be used to assess their understanding at the end of the activities.

Opportunities for IT

Children could use a word processor or desktop publishing package to write their own labels to go on the large water cycle display. The elements of the display could describe what is happening at different points in the cycle. Children could be given an opportunity to try using different fonts and sizes to create a label that is readable from a distance.

Children could also use a CD-ROM to find out more about the water cycle, water treatment and reservoirs. In order to do this, children will need to know how to save text from the CD-ROM and then reload it on to their word processor. This will differ depending on the actual computer, CD-ROM and word processor. Once the text is loaded, children should edit it by deleting unwanted text, adding links to different sections. It would be a good idea to discuss with the class beforehand what kind of information will be needed, or to give a limited number of words (say 100) so that they have to decide for themselves the most important information. This 'editorial' work could be done away from the computer using a highlighter pen on a printout of the text. Once the children have decided on the text, they could return and retrieve their saved text to edit it and print it out for the display.

Children could use an art or drawing package to create their own picture of the water cycle with labels for the different parts. Alternatively, the teacher could provide a file with the drawing already completed and the children can be shown how to add labels to the picture. If this is done with a drawing package, children can write the text for the label, move the text to the correct position and then draw a line to link it to

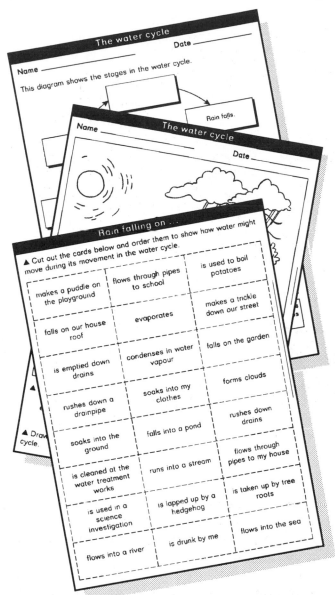

who have not done this kind of work before may need considerable support to start with and an extra pair of hands to work with the computer group will enable the children to concentrate on the task rather than any problems that may arise.

Display ideas
Create a huge representation of the water cycle to which all the class can contribute.

Reference to photocopiable sheets
The boxes on photocopiable sheet 138 can be cut out, rearranged and later stuck on a larger piece of paper so that the children can connect them with arrows to show water cycles. The title can be completed by adding the name of your school, village or area. Sheet 139 provides a representation of the water cycle which can be used for discussion before the children write the given words in the correct positions. Sheet 140 can be used for support, and also used at the end of the work on the water cycle as an assessment task.

BURNING MATERIALS

Changes which occur as a result of burning cannot be reversed.

✝✝ *Teacher demonstration to whole class, sharing observations, individual recording.*

🕐 *20–30 minutes for demonstration; 30 minutes for recording.*

Previous skills/knowledge needed
Children should be aware of the dangers of burning materials, and understand the need for safety procedures. Not only is there the danger of the heat, but a danger from any poisonous gases produced.

the appropriate part of the picture. The labelled picture can then be printed out for the child's folder or a class display.

A more ambitious project would be to make a multimedia presentation about the water cycle using authoring software. This might start with an opening page showing a picture of the water cycle with different parts highlighted. When the child clicks with the mouse on a highlighted part, he is taken to another screen giving more details about that particular part of the water cycle. Screens could contain text, pictures, sounds and even moving pictures taken with a video camera. Children can add their own voices using a microphone attached to the computer and suitable software.

The initial structure could be set up by the teacher in advance and the children then divided into groups, with each one responsible for a different part of the presentation. The page planning could be done away from the computer so that the group can design their own screen layout, decide what text and pictures they want to use and collect these together before they start work on the computer. Children

Key background information

Burning requires oxygen; heat and gas are produced; usually some unburnt particles remain; there may also be solid products of burning (ash).

Preparation

Decide on a safe area for demonstrating the burning process and organise any necessary safety measures. Collect the equipment (see below) and firmly fasten the candle in a holder or at the centre of a large foil dish. Prepare a chart on the board to record the results.

Resources needed

A large metal tray containing sand, to provide a safe area from which to work; foil dishes; a candle in a holder; matches; a pair of tongs; materials to burn such as small pieces of paper, fabric, a twig, string, a paper drinking straw (avoid any material which might give off harmful fumes although a small piece of plastic could be used).

What to do

Arrange the class so that everyone can see the demonstration and is safely seated. Explain that you are going to light the candle and use it to burn various materials, and that the children should observe carefully. Choose two children to write the class's observations on the prepared chart on the board after each material is burned.

Using the tongs, set alight the first material, holding it over a foil dish in the tray of sand while it burns. Encourage comments on the appearance of the flame, the smoke and any gas observed or noise heard. As small pieces of material are being used, the flames will soon die away and any residue which is still held by the tongs or has fallen into the dish can be observed. Continue until all samples have been burned,

and use a different foil dish for each material so that anything remaining from the burning can be examined. Encourage the children's observations on the burning candle; notice what happens to the wax.

Ask them if any of the burned materials could be 'brought back', and if any new materials were produced. Point out that the gases produced will have disappeared into the atmosphere.

As a follow-up to this activity, and to stress the importance of safety, make a survey of the school's fire-fighting equipment, checking the locations of extinguishers and fire blankets. Find out how they should be used.

Suggestion(s) for extension

Demonstrate the importance of oxygen in the burning process by inverting a glass jar over a burning candle. The candle will go out when the restricted oxygen supply has been used up. Link this to methods of fire fighting which rely on limiting the supply of oxygen.

Collect examples of materials which burn and cause major pollution, such as chemicals, burning tyres and oil spills set alight.

Suggestion(s) for support

Completing the chart as a class will help develop all the children's recording skills.

Assessment opportunities

As the activity progresses and while the children are completing their recording, talk to individuals to check their understanding of the process of burning as a change which is not reversible.

Opportunities for IT

Pairs of children could use a word processor to write about one of the materials burnt. They could use the information collected from the rest of the class to help them with their observations. The final description could be printed out, possibly with a picture or piece of the material itself and any ashes (sealed under clear adhesive tape) attached and displayed on the wall or in a class folder on burning materials.

Children could use an art or graphics package to create their own poster on fire safety as a result of this activity. They could also use a word processor to explain how to put out a fire. The original ideas could be entered on the computer and then reorganised to create a final account which could be printed out.

Display ideas

Make a display featuring pictures which show the effects of burning on buildings, forests and grasslands.

Other aspects of the Science PoS covered

Experimental and Investigative Science – 2b; 3a, b, c, e.

Separating mixtures

The activities in this section involve examining, investigating and comparing soluble and insoluble materials and the process required in order to separate these materials. Saturated solutions are also investigated. Children are introduced to basic scientific terms which explain the processes they are exploring. Opportunities arise for devising and carrying out separation by sieving, filtering and evaporating.

Throughout these activities, children are encouraged to use their experience and understanding of the processes of dissolving and evaporating to ask questions, make predictions and work independently and responsibly. Guidance with recording offered in the activities will help children to plan their work and draw relevant conclusions.

77

MATERIALS

MAKING AND SORTING MIXTURES

A mixture can have particles of different sizes.

†† *Class discussion, followed by children working in pairs.*

🕐 *Allow a period of a few days while the mixtures are being collected, then 30 to 40 minutes for sorting and recording.*

Previous skills/knowledge needed
Children will need to understand the meanings of the words *particles* and *mixture*, and can be reminded of these in the introductory discussion. They will need to work co-operatively with a partner and be aware of the dangers of putting small objects in their mouths.

Key background information
Some solids are made up of small distinguishable particles; usually the particles are of a similar size and form, such as those of sand and sugar. Sometimes particles of various sizes occur together as mixtures, either naturally as with soils or pebbles, or in man-made form as with a button collection or a handful of coins. By examining and sorting mixtures with large particles which can be handled, children will more readily understand the composition of those mixtures they will be working with later, but which are not so easy to observe.

Preparation
Collect samples of mixtures and make up any others you feel might be helpful.

Resources needed
A wide variety of mixtures, such as pebble mixes, dried vegetable mixtures, assortments of nails, confetti, buttons, crayon oddments and coins; blindfolds; a stopwatch; photocopiable sheet 141 (one copy for each child).

What to do
Show the children one of the mixtures and ask them what other mixtures they can think of. If possible, allow a period of a few days while the children create mixtures of their own to add to the collection. When enough mixtures are available, ask the children which mixtures they think will be the easiest to sort by hand. Let them test

their predictions using only their fingers. What is it that makes one mixture easier to sort than another? Is it a greater difference in size between the particles? Could colour have anything to do with the ease of sorting? Does it depend on how many different types of particle there are in the mixture?

After these initial investigations, let pairs of children devise time tests for others. They could use a cupful of the mixture each time, and use extensive trialling to find out the fastest sorting time and the easiest mixture to sort. The children can use photocopiable sheet 141 for recording, commenting on the various shapes and sizes of particles and the ease of sorting.

Suggestion(s) for extension
Ask the children to wear blindfolds and to try sorting by touch only. Do they still find the same mixtures the easiest to sort?

Suggestion(s) for support
Write down the names of the ingredients which make up the mixture for those children who need help to complete the photocopiable sheet.

Assessment opportunities
As individual children are working, assess their ability to organise a task and work co-operatively.

Display ideas
Include as many mixtures as possible in a 'mixtures' display for the children to handle safely.

Other aspects of the Science PoS covered
Experimental and Investigative Science – 1b; 2b, c; 3b, c, d, e.

Reference to photocopiable sheet
Photocopiable sheet 141 asks children to describe four mixtures that they have tested and to record their conclusions.

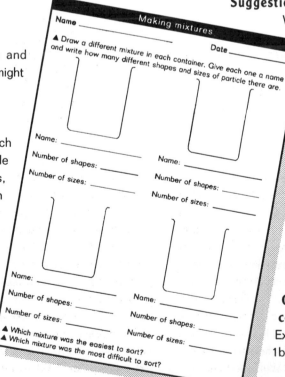

MATERIALS

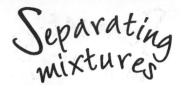

METHODS OF SORTING

Different-sized particles in a mixture can be separated by sieving.

†† *Whole class for introduction and discussion, followed by children working in small groups of three or four. Allow time for demonstrations and evaluation at the end of the task.*

🕐 *Up to an hour for discussion, planning and trialling; another hour for testing, recording, demonstrating and evaluating.*

Previous skills/knowledge needed

Pupils will need to be able to work efficiently in groups, sharing ideas and tasks within the activity. Their experiences of separating materials by sieving will vary, but an introductory discussion will help to provide a basis from which to begin.

Key background information

Sieves and strainers are widely used as an efficient means of separating different-sized particles from each other.

Preparation

Make up a variety of mixtures, each with three different ingredients of differing sizes – such as dried peas, beans and lentils, or pebbles, rice and sand. It might be possible to give each group a mixture with a different combination of ingredients. Prepare a set of questions to help with planning and evaluating.

Resources needed

A collection of different sieves and strainers, and meshes of varying weaves; ingredients for mixtures such as dried peas, beans and lentils, pebbles, beads, marbles, grit, sand, small buttons, beads and soil; two jars or plastic containers per group; card; scissors; elastic bands; a stapler.

What to do

Tell the children that you want them to devise a method of separating the particles in a mixture where the particles are small and using hands would not be efficient. Show them an example of a mixture you have prepared and encourage them to put forward their ideas. Ask them to think of examples of separating they might have seen or used themselves – these might include using sieves in cooking and gardening. Discuss the different types of sieves and strainers the children have seen and show the equipment you have collected. Compare the size, shapes and patterns of the holes in the sieves and consider the task each sieve was designed for. Ask the children what materials they would use to make their own sieve. Suggestions will include fabrics of various weaves such as mesh and netting, pieces from tights, curtains and onion bags. Demonstrate and examine the samples you have collected. Perhaps the children know of others.

Now give each group a (different) mixture. Ask them to plan a strategy for separating the ingredients of the mixtures, which they will eventually demonstrate to the rest of the class. Tell them whether they can use the ready-made equipment or whether you want them to make their own sieving device. Encourage the group to examine the mixture carefully and to consider what type of sieve would be most appropriate for the sizes of the particles. Which particles will they remove first? Is the order in which they remove the types of particle going to be important? Perhaps some retrialling will be necessary. Make the sieves and strainers available for the children to experiment with, even if they will eventually be making their own devices. These items could be arranged on a display table which children can use for reference or simple trialling.

Emphasise that this is still the planning stage and not yet the time for making and testing. Check that each group is progressing with their planning and encourage the children to think clearly about each stage of the separating process. Which particles have they decided to remove first? Which is the best sieve for the job? Which container will collect the particles as they are sieved? When they have just two types of particles left, how will these be separated? Have they thought about the containers they will use? How can the children make sure none of the mixture is spilt? Will time be needed to make their own sieving device? Do they need any extra equipment? When the plan is complete, children can write down what they intend to do. Questions to guide their recording could include: What are you trying to do? What equipment will you need? Have you carried out any trials? What is your plan?

MATERIALS

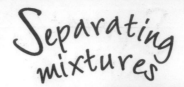

Any group making their own sieves will need extra time; children using manufactured sieves and strainers will need to search out the right sizes of container to use for their test. Time taken for the testing will also vary depending on the success of the sieving process. Children might want to change their plans if problems arise or if they think of better ideas. They will want to try out their chosen method several times before demonstrating it to the rest of the class. Encourage the children to record the successful elements of their experiments, also including any problems they might have encountered and suggestions for further improvements. Questions to prompt their thinking might include: How well did your plan work? What problems did you have? Could you have improved your separating method in any way?

As each group demonstrates its method to the rest of the class, point out good techniques and co-operative working.

Suggestion(s) for extension
Challenge a group of children to separate a mixture with four, five or six ingredients.

Suggestion(s) for support
Provide a more detailed list of headings in the form of questions to guide children through the processes of planning and recording.

Assessment opportunities
Observe children's ability to generate ideas, work co-operatively and efficiently, understand the need for retrialling and overcoming problems.

Display ideas
Display the children's plans and recording in a special area of the room. Pin up the work rather than fixing it permanently, to give a workshop feel and to show that alterations and improvements can be made at any stage. If possible, provide equipment and ingredients so that children can try out each other's ideas. Include examples of sieves and strainers with labels indicating their uses in everyday life.

Other examples of the Science PoS covered
Experimental and Investigative Science – 1a, b, e; 2a, b, c; 3e.

MIXING MATERIALS WITH WATER

Some solids dissolve in water.

†† *Discussion and teacher demonstration to whole class followed by children working in pairs or small groups. It is important to end the session by sharing comments and results.*

🕐 *One hour.*

⚠ *Warn the children that it can be dangerous to taste unknown materials.*

Previous skills/knowledge needed
The children must understand clearly what is meant by dissolving, and a demonstration during the introduction to the activity will remind them of this process. Help to devise questions or statements that the children can refer to during testing to determine whether a material has dissolved or not. For example: Is the water cloudy? Is there a sediment left at the bottom of the container? If so, the material has not dissolved. Is the water clear and is nothing left at the bottom of the container? If so, the material has dissolved.

Key background information
Materials which dissolve in a liquid are described as being soluble in that liquid. Materials which do not dissolve are therefore insoluble. A dissolved material and the liquid in which it is dissolved make a solution; the insoluble material together with the liquid make a mixture. Materials which do not dissolve in water might dissolve in other liquids.

Preparation
Put supplies of the materials to be tested in containers marked A to H (if eight samples are to be used) so that at this stage, children do not know what the materials are. Also provide the spoons, transparent containers for mixing, and water. Work out the ideal amounts of water and material to use. This will depend on the size of the container – enough material is needed to show the sediment easily if it is insoluble, but not enough to saturate the solution if the material is soluble. Add the water to the jars if this is more convenient than asking the children to do so.

Resources needed
A quantity of safe transparent containers is required so that each group can have one for each material to be tested (small baby food jars with lids are ideal); a variety of materials for testing, some of which are soluble in water (such as sugar, salt, bath salts, coffee powder), and some of which are insoluble (such as flour, sand, talcum powder, powdered chalk); plastic spoons; containers for water; hand-lenses and labels; photocopiable sheets 142 and 143 (one copy for each child).

What to do

Display the containers of 'mystery' materials. Explain to the children that you want them to find out whether each material dissolves in water. Discuss what is meant by dissolving. Remind the children with a demonstration to show how a soluble material dissolves in water, leaving a clear solution with no sediment at the bottom of the container; while an insoluble material remains suspended in the water, forming a sediment at the bottom as it settles and making a mixture. Use the terms *soluble*, *insoluble*, *solution*, *mixture*, and *sediment*, so that the children can get used to them as they carry out the tests. Discuss a strategy for working which will involve the groups of children trying each material in turn. First, it is important to label the jars with the code letter of the material being tested. Then the material can be added to the water and stirred, and observations and a decision can be made. Allow each group time to discuss and record the plan using photocopiable sheet 142.

Before each test, encourage the children to use a hand-lens to examine and describe the material, writing their observations on a chart together with the results. Photocopiable sheet 143 can be used for this purpose.

When testing is complete the jars can be grouped according to whether they contain a solution or a mixture. Compare the results as a class. Finally, ask the children if they have identified any of the mystery materials. Reveal the names, which can be added to the chart. As a summary, children can sort the named materials into soluble and insoluble groups.

Suggestion(s) for extension

Find out what is meant by hard and soft water, and what is dissolved in water to make it hard.

Collect examples of instances when we take dissolving for granted in everyday life, such as sweeteners in drinks, salt in cooking and bath salts in water.

Find out how dissolved sugar can affect teeth.

Suggestion(s) for support

Where necessary, help children to write a list of step-by-step instructions which they can follow when carrying out the test.

Assessment opportunities

Assess the children's understanding of the dissolving process as they work, either by discussion or by observation. Assess their ability to work efficiently and to record accurately.

Display ideas

Arrange the jars of mixtures and solutions so they can be examined and compared. Write out the key words 'soluble', 'insoluble', 'sediment', 'mixture', 'solution', and pin these up for reference.

Other aspects of the Science PoS covered

Experimental and Investigative Science – 1a, c, e; 2a, b; 3b, c, e.

Reference to photocopiable sheets

Photocopiable sheet 142 asks children to describe in diagram form what happens when materials are mixed with water, and also provides a planning framework; sheet 143 provides a chart for recording observations, results and a summary.

RECOVERING MATERIAL FROM A MIXTURE

An insoluble solid can be separated from a liquid by filtering.

†† *Discussion and demonstration to whole class, followed by children working in pairs or small groups.*

⏰ *One hour.*

Previous skills/knowledge needed

If children use the mixtures made during the previous activity, they will more easily understand the filtering process which follows.

Key background information

The particles of a material which does not dissolve in water remain suspended in the liquid and gradually form a sediment at the bottom of the mixture. These particles can be removed if the liquid is poured through a mesh, the holes of which allow the water to pass through but are too small to allow the particles of the material to pass.

Preparation

Put cutlery with water in a washing-up bowl, beads or marbles in a smaller container with water, and a burst tea-bag with water in a cup. Make funnels, if necessary, from plastic drinks bottles. If mixtures are not available from the previous activity, make more by mixing an insoluble material with water.

Resources needed

Beads or marbles; a selection of safe spoons and forks; a large bowl; a smaller container (perhaps a saucepan); a colander, sieve or strainer; funnels; paper towels or kitchen roll; small containers to collect the water after filtering; hand-lenses.

What to do

Show the class the washing-up bowl containing spoons and forks and a quantity of water. Explain that you have been washing up and need to get all the cutlery out of the bowl. Ask a child to do this for you and encourage them to 'scoop' rather than 'pick' out the cutlery. Ask the rest of the children to describe the technique, and suggest that the fingers have been used as a sieve. Next, produce the container of beads and water and ask what would be a useful piece of equipment for separating the beads from the water. Let a child demonstrate this with the colander. Finally, show the children a burst tea-bag in a cup of water, and this time separate the particles from the liquid with a strainer.

Now introduce to the children the challenge of recovering the very small particles from their (previously made) mixtures. Remind them that if the material can still be seen in the water, then it is insoluble. Ask for suggestions as to what could be used to hold back the very small particles. If kitchen-towel paper is to be used, how will it be held in place? The most secure method is to use a funnel. How will the water be collected? Explain that when paper or fabric with a very fine mesh is used as a sieve to separate a solid from a liquid, the process is called *filtering*.

Allow the groups time to discuss the plan and to practise lining the funnel with the kitchen towel. Can they see any holes in the kitchen towel with a hand-lens? Questions and headings to guide the children's recording could include: How can filtering help to remove a material from a liquid? Describe how you will separate the material. What equipment will you need?

At this stage the test can be carried out. How successful was the kitchen roll at holding back the particles? Is the water really clear now? Perhaps the water needs to be poured through the filter again. Can the insoluble material be seen on the kitchen roll? Encourage children to examine the contents of the piece of kitchen roll carefully. It should be allowed to dry and then re-examined. Tell the children to label the two separated materials and display them for others to see. Questions which will help children to complete their recording could include: Was your filtering successful? How clear was the water? Where is the insoluble material?

MATERIALS

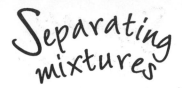

Suggestion(s) for extension

Challenge groups of children to devise a filtering system for cleaning muddy water. Which system produces the cleanest water?

Find out about the filtering processes involved in the treatment of water and arrange a visit to the local water treatment works.

Suggestion(s) for support

Provide extra help with planning and recording in cases where children find it difficult to work systematically.

Assessment opportunities

Check that the children understand the process of filtering, and that the insoluble material has remained unchanged throughout the mixing and filtering processes.

Display ideas

Provide books and pictures which show the workings of filter beds at a water treatment works. Display filter systems designed by the children or yourself.

Other aspects of the Science PoS covered

Experimental and Investigative Science – 1a, e; 2a, b, c; 3c, e.

RECOVERING A DISSOLVED MATERIAL

A dissolved solid can be recovered by evaporating the liquid in which it is dissolved.

†† *Whole-class introduction, followed by children working in pairs or small groups.*

🕐 *45 minutes for discussion, testing and recording; allow one to two days for evaporation to occur, then 30 minutes for observations, further discussion and recording.*

⚠ *Warn the children that solutions should not be tasted.*

Previous skills/knowledge needed

Children will need to have experienced and understood the processes of dissolving and evaporating. If they can use the solutions they made during a previous activity, they can follow the cycle of mixing two materials and then separating them.

Key background information

The molecules of a material soluble in water spread out and fill spaces between the molecules of the water. They become part of a solution with the water and cannot be removed by the filtering process. As evaporation occurs and the water molecules escape into the air, the solid material remains. Some materials re-form as crystals.

Preparation

If the solutions from a previous activity are not available, prepare more by mixing a soluble material with water.

Resources needed

Funnels; kitchen roll; containers; flat dishes or saucers.

What to do

Ask the children what they think will happen if they filter the solutions they have made previously. Either demonstrate this with a solution or give the groups the opportunity to do the test for themselves. What remains on the filter paper? Where is the soluble material? Is the liquid any different after filtering? When the children understand that there is nothing left on the kitchen paper and that the solution is still intact, ask for suggestions as to how the water could be separated from the soluble material. If the children have previously explored evaporation, they may suggest evaporating their solutions. Prompt the children's thinking by asking: How can evaporation be made to happen more quickly? What type of container is it best to use and where is a good spot to leave them? Questions to help with recording could include: What happened when the solution was filtered? Where was the solid material? Where was the liquid? Was this method successful in separating the materials? What is your plan now? What do you think will happen this time?

Allow the children to carry out the experiment, and encourage frequent observations while evaporation proceeds. What has happened to the water? Make sure that the children realise that although the water is no longer evident and has not been collected, it has been separated from the soluble material. Encourage the children to examine the material which is left on the saucer. Is the soluble material in exactly the same form as it was before the solution was made? Provide some of the original material for comparison. It is

possible that crystals will have formed as a result of evaporation; the patterns these make can be sketched. If different solutions were used, the crystal shapes can be compared. Observations should be recorded. Questions to guide recording could include: How was the material separated from the liquid? Where is the water? Where is the soluble material?

Suggestion(s) for extension

Try growing crystals from other solutions using copper sulphate, ferrous sulphate and chrome alum, but supervise this closely.

Find out about how salt is obtained from seas and mines.

Suggestion(s) for support

Devise a structured set of questions where necessary to help children with planning and recording.

Assessment opportunities

To assess the children's understanding, listen to their descriptions of evaporation and the part it plays in the separation of the materials which make a solution.

Display ideas

Exhibit the evaporating liquid and display pictures and drawings of different crystal formations. Arrange the key words around the display for reference.

Other aspects of the Science PoS covered

Experimental and Investigative Science – 1a, b, e; 2a; 3b, c, d, e.

MAKING A SATURATED SOLUTION

There is a limit to the mass of solid that can dissolve in a certain amount of water.

†† *Whole-class discussion, followed by children working in pairs or small groups.*

🕐 *45 minutes to one hour for discussion, planning and recording; up to one hour for testing, comparing results and concluding.*

⚠ *Warn children that solutions should not be tasted.*

Previous skills/knowledge needed

Children will need to have explored the process of dissolving.

Key background information

A soluble material will continue to dissolve in an amount of water until the molecules of the soluble material can no longer find spaces to move into. When this point is reached, a sediment of the material will remain.

Preparation

Try out the test beforehand if possible, to find out how long it will take and the amounts of soluble material that will be used.

Resources needed

Two containers for each group (one for mixing, one to hold the soluble material); spoons, containers with a measuring scale in millilitres (ml); equipment for measuring grams; sugar or other soluble materials; photocopiable sheets 144 and 145 (one copy per child).

What to do

Explain to the children that you want them to find out how much of a soluble material can be dissolved in water, but that first they should share ideas and decide on a good way of working.

If they keep adding sugar to water, will it always dissolve? Discuss increasing the amount of water so that more sugar will dissolve; why is this suggestion not helpful? How can you find out how much sugar will dissolve in a certain amount of water, a cupful for instance? How will you know if the soluble material is no longer dissolving? How much of the material will you add to the water each time? Is it important to know this? How will you remember how much of the material has been added to the liquid? What needs to be kept the same to make the test fair? Exactly how will the sugar be added? Will stirring be involved? Will you want to stir the solution the same number of times each time more is added? What will need to be measured? Children will need time to think through their strategy and discuss a systematic method of working. A small amount of water should be used

same amount of soluble material been used by all the groups? If not, are there reasons for this? Did techniques differ at all? Do any interesting patterns emerge? Did the number of stirs needed each time stay the same? Explain that when no further soluble material will dissolve, we say that the solution has become *saturated*.

Children should complete the activity by recording their conclusions, drawing graphs if data are available.

Suggestion(s) for extension
Find out if temperature has any effect on the amount of soluble material that will dissolve in a certain amount of water.

Suggestion(s) for support
To simplify this activity, ask children to stir spoonfuls of a soluble material into an amount of water until it will no longer dissolve. Help with recording.

Assessment opportunities
Assess children's understanding of the process of dissolving, their ability to work with equipment efficiently, and their skill at recognising patterns and interpreting results.

(100ml to 200ml depending on the size of container), and the soluble material can be added in grams or small level spoonfuls. Children might decide to give the same number of stirs each time, or count how many stirs are required each time to get the material to dissolve. Allow time for the children to record their plan and prepare a chart to collect their results. Photocopiable sheets 144 and 145 provide a framework and chart for this purpose.

Encourage the children to develop a co-operative and efficient method of working, sharing the aspects of the task among themselves and recording systematically. Check each group to make sure that they recognise the dissolving process and know that when the soluble material no longer disappears, it is no longer dissolving. If several, or all, of the groups use the same soluble material, then useful comparisons can be made later.

When all testing is complete, look at each group's results. Do any patterns emerge? Has the

Opportunities for IT
If the whole class investigates just one or two different soluble substances, there should be enough results to plot a graph using graphing software. The resultant graph can be used as a basis for discussing how fair the test has been, why different groups had different results and what the average result might be.

Display ideas
Present children's planning and results for reference. Draw a large graph to represent the results of all the groups.

Other aspects of the Science PoS covered
Experimental and Investigative Science – 1a, c; 2a, b; 3a, b, c, e.

Reference to photocopiable sheet
Photocopiable sheet 144 provides a framework for planning and sheet 145 a chart for recording results and observations.

Saturated solutions

Name _____

Amount of material we added each time	How many stirs before the material dissolved	Date _____ Observations and comments

---

Dissolving a material in water

Name _____   Date _____

What do we want to find out?

How are we going to carry out our test?

How will we know when the material is no longer dissolving?

What we will need to measure:

What we will need to keep the same each time:

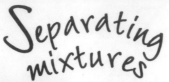

COMPARING SATURATED SOLUTIONS

The limit to the mass of solid which can dissolve in an amount of water is different for different solids.

†† *Whole-class discussion, followed by children working in pairs or small groups.*

🕐 *One hour.*

⚠ *Warn children that solutions should not be tasted.*

Previous skills/knowledge needed
Children will need to have explored the process of dissolving and completed the previous activity.

Preparation
Try out the test beforehand to find out which amounts of water and soluble materials are most suitable for the containers being used.

Resources needed
Two small containers for each group; spoons; equipment for measuring small amounts of the soluble materials; different soluble materials (such as sugar, salt, bath salts).

What to do
Remind children of the previous activity, and tell them that you now want to know if the same amount of other soluble materials will dissolve in water before the solution becomes saturated. Ask for suggestions as to how this could be achieved. Children will want to repeat the previous test using a different soluble material. Suggest a comparative test, with children testing two materials at the same time, perhaps using spoonfuls and smaller amounts of liquid to achieve a quicker result. What must be kept the same if the test is to be fair? What is the factor which must be different? Give the groups the opportunity to plan, record and prepare a chart for their results before testing begins. Encourage the children to use their experience of the previous activity when carrying out this test. If different materials are tested by other groups further comparisons can be made.

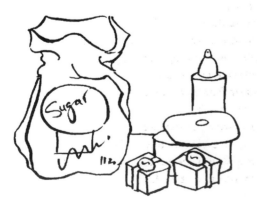

After testing, allow time for discussion and making comparisons. Children will conclude that the amounts of different soluble materials that will dissolve in a certain amount of liquid are not the same. Consider how useful this information is to us. Discuss the importance of using the right amounts of soluble materials that we use in everyday tasks, and of reading the instructions on packets of soluble materials in order to use the correct amount.

Encourage children to display their results as a graph.

Suggestion(s) for extension
Find out more about the amounts of soluble materials that are recommended to be mixed with water; collect instructions on packets. Consider the consequences of using the wrong amounts.

Suggestion(s) for support
Provide step-by-step instructions for children to follow, where this is necessary.

Assessment opportunities
Assess individual children's ability to make comparisons and to relate the activity to everyday situations.

Opportunities for IT
The results from each group can be displayed as a graph using graph-plotting software. The results could also be recorded using a simple spreadsheet which can also display the results graphically.

The spreadsheet might look like this:

	a	b	c
1	**Group**	**Salt**	**Sugar**
2	Gp1	5	6
3	Gp2	3	4
4	Gp3	4	4
5	Gp4	5	6
6			
7	Average	ave (b2:b5)	ave (c2:c5)

The results could be averaged out to provide a more consistent result from the whole class. This should be discussed with the children and the formula added into the spreadsheet can be explained.

Display ideas
Display any graphs the children have drawn and create a class graph to show the results of all the groups.

Other aspects of the Science PoS covered
Experimental and Investigative Science – 1a, c, d, e; 2a, b, c; 3a, b, c, d.

MATERIALS

Investigations

Scientific understanding involves knowledge of both the content of science and the methods by which that knowledge is obtained. Experimental and Investigative Science requires children to develop the intellectual and practical skills which will allow them to explore and investigate the world of science, and develop a fuller understanding of scientific phenomena, the nature of the theories explaining these phenomena and the procedures of scientific investigation. This should be achieved through activities that require a progressively more systematic and quantitative approach, developing and drawing on an increasing knowledge and understanding of science.

This section contains several activities which provide the children with an opportunity to plan and carry out investigations in which they:

▲ ask questions, predict and hypothesise;
▲ observe, measure and manipulate variables;
▲ interpret results and evaluate scientific evidence.

Within the context of their growing knowledge of physical processes, these activities will allow children to gain awareness both of the nature of scientific activity and of the basis on which scientific claims are made.

The activities here are necessarily more open-ended than those in other sections of the book, but guidance is given with regard to classroom management, the concepts likely to emerge and how you can use the activities for assessment purposes.

MATERIALS

INVESTIGATING STRENGTH

Which material makes the strongest bag?

†† *Children working in pairs or small groups.*

🕐 *One hour for discussion, planning and recording; one hour for testing, recording and drawing conclusions.*

⚠ *Children will need to work sensibly and carefully when handling the fairly heavy loads.*

Previous skills/knowledge needed

Children need to understand the concept of strength and know that a material demonstrating strength is tough, can resist forces and will support heavy loads.

Key background information

We rely on construction materials for their strength. What we are able to achieve technically is limited by the weakness of materials, as in the construction of bridges, buildings, ships and aircraft. Through the ages, metals have been valued as the strongest of materials, but now synthetic materials of greater strength and lightness have been developed. It would be difficult for children to test the strengths of certain materials, but it is possible for them to compare different types of a particular material or to compare materials which are quite similar.

Preparation

Collect paper, plastic and fabric bags, or materials to make these with. Anticipate that the children will use carrier-sized bags, and test these with sand, marbles or other materials beforehand to make sure they are suitable for testing.

Resources needed

Sand or marbles; different types of plastic, paper and fabric bags or materials to make bags; trays, buckets or newspaper.

What to do

Discuss with the children what is meant by strength. Ask if they think paper is a strong material. If they compare paper with metal, the answer will be 'no'. Encourage them to consider different types of paper. Can they think of an instance where paper needs to be strong? Which types of paper are less strong?

Tell the children that you want them to test different bags to compare their strengths – paper bags can be used, also plastic bags and perhaps ones made of fabric. Ask for suggestions as to how a test could be carried out. Show the children some examples of bags you have collected. Which ones could be tested for strength? What will the test be? How will it be made fair? Bags to be tested should be as similar in size and design as possible. If the children are not happy with your selection of bags, they can look around for other examples or even use the material of which the bags are made to make more standard versions of their own.

Move on to the test itself. What would be a workable method for testing the strength of a bag? As bags are being tested, the children will probably want to know how successful they are at holding things, especially a heavy load. What could be used to represent the contents of the bags? Steer the children towards considering a uniform material to use – something which can be added gradually, such as sand or marbles. How will the children decide which bag material is the strongest? Suggestions will include filling the bag until it splits, tears or gives way. How will this be done fairly? Will any measuring be involved? How will the bag be supported? How will the test be made safe? If the bag is going to tear or split, what will happen to the contents? Children might consider suspending the bags from a hook, a door handle or a specially designed piece of apparatus, or holding the bags in their hands. Give the groups of children the opportunity to discuss, formulate and record their plan.

Headings for recording could include:
▲ What we want to find out.
▲ What we think will happen.
▲ How we will carry out the investigation.
▲ What equipment we will use.
▲ How we will make the test fair.
▲ How we will make the test safe.
▲ What we will need to measure.

As the children devise their tests, encourage them to work systematically and to share the task co-operatively among the members of the group. Questions to guide their thinking might include: Which bags are you going to test? How are you going to support the bags? If one member of the group is going to hold them, have you worked out a method which will be the fairest possible? If the bags are to be suspended

MATERIALS

from a handle, are you sure there is no unfair support provided by the bag touching the door? How will the 'heavy' material be added to the bags? What quantities will be added each time? What will you be looking for? Are you prepared for the bag breaking? How will you collect your results? A chart should be devised which will allow comparisons between bags to be made. Figure 1 shows one possible method for this.

When the children know exactly how they will proceed, the testing can begin. Check that the groups are following their plan. If not, why have changes in the procedure been made? Are the changes improvements? Encourage safe working, though if small bags are being used the weight of material in the bags will not be great. Make sure that the children record their observations for each part of the test in detail, observing closely what happens each time an amount of material is added to the bag.

When testing is complete, discuss the results as a class. Are the children satisfied with the results? Were the results as expected? Were there any surprises? Can any comparisons be drawn between the groups? Are there any conflicting results? What could be the explanation for this? Did the groups encounter any problems? Were these overcome? Would another, improved test be a good idea? Is there anything further they would like to investigate? Encourage the children to write a summary of their results.

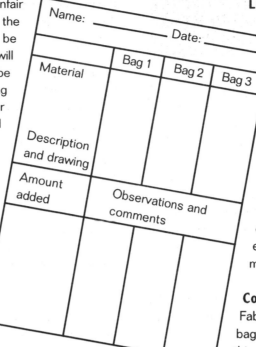

Name: _____ Date: _____			
Material	Bag 1	Bag 2	Bag 3
Description and drawing			
Amount added	Observations and comments		

Figure 1

Likely problems

Any difficulty in finding similar bags to test can be overcome by making ones specially for the tests. A large bag can be used to create a smaller one by folding the edges and stapling these together. Handles can be attached, using the same numbers and positions of staples for each bag to ensure fairness. The handles of any bags can be a problem; if they prove to be the weak point, the fact that they give way can be considered as part of the evidence if they are made of the same material as the rest of the bag.

Concepts likely to emerge

Fabric is a strong material used for making bags. Plastic and paper are widely used for this purpose, and their strength varies considerably depending on the quality and thickness of the materials. Some plastics are stronger than paper and some papers are stronger than plastic. The children will discover which particular type of plastic or paper is the strongest out of those they have tested.

Using the activity for assessment

All aspects of Experimental and Investigative Science are covered by this investigation. A group of children could be assessed on their ability to turn ideas into a form which can be investigated, ensuring a fair and safe test, and on their skill at observing, measuring and presenting evidence.

Other investigations

▲ Which type of thread or string is the strongest?

MATERIALS

◈ INSULATING MATERIALS

Which materials are best for preventing heat from escaping?

✝✝ *Children working in groups of four or five.*

🕐 *One hour for planning, preparing and recording; one hour for testing and concluding.*

⚠ *Care will be needed when hot liquids are used.*

Previous skills/knowledge needed

Children will need to understand that heat is always travelling from its source to a cooler area, and that we often need to try to prevent this (where possible). They may have briefly explored the properties of materials which are thermal insulators. Children will also need to be able to read a thermometer.

Key background information

The molecules of some materials are less affected by the presence of heat than others. They do not warm up and vibrate as easily as those in other materials and therefore do not pass the heat through the material. These materials are poor conductors of heat and so are good insulators, and are often used for this purpose in the home. In this test, plastic cups are placed in tins (or other containers) which give sufficient space for the insulating material to be packed around the cup. Hot water will be poured into the cups and the temperature taken at regular intervals.

Preparation

Collect identical containers into each of which a plastic cup and some insulating material can be fitted. Large baby food tins or dog food tins can be used if there are no sharp edges.

Resources needed

Large tins or other suitable containers; plastic cups; thermometers; watches or stopwatches; recording charts based on Figure 2.

What to do

Tell the children that you want them to find out which materials are the best at preventing heat escaping from a cup of hot liquid – that is, which materials are the best thermal insulators. Ask for suggestions as to how this investigation could be organised. How can a test using hot liquids be carried out safely? Suggest that plastic cups are to be used and that materials to be tested will be packed around the cups. Show the children the large tins or other containers in which the cups and the packing will be contained. Ask them what factors will need to be kept the same if the test is to be fair. How will they know which materials are most successful at preventing the heat from escaping? How will the temperature be measured? How often will the temperature be measured? What precautions are important if the test is to be carried out safely?

The children can decide which materials they would like to test. From their experience of exploring the properties of thermal insulation, suggestions might include newspaper, polystyrene chips, wood shavings or sawdust, plastic beads, sheep's fleece, feathers and small pieces of fabric. One cup can be left with no insulating material.

Explain to the children that you will pour the water into the cups at the appropriate time. Each person in the group could be responsible for organising one of the insulation materials. Allow the groups time to plan, prepare and record their investigation; as the children do this, discuss their choice of materials. Have they chosen a wide variety of materials? Which one do they think will be the best insulator? Have they considered how firmly they will pack the materials? Have they thought about how much hot water they will need in the cups? How can they make sure you give them the right amount of water? How often will they measure the temperature? Will they each read one thermometer? Is it necessary to double-check readings? Who will do the timing between readings? How will they record the measurements?

Name: ________________							Date: ________
			Temperatures				
Insulating materials	Start	After 5 minutes	After 10 minutes	After 15 minutes	After 20 minutes	After 25 minutes	After 30 minutes
No insulating material used							
Sample and description of material							
Sample and description of material							
Sample and description of material							
Sample and description of material							

Figure 2

Headings to guide recording could include:

- ▲ What we want to find out.
- ▲ What we think will happen.
- ▲ How we will carry out the investigation.
- ▲ How we will make sure the test is safe.
- ▲ What equipment we will use.
- ▲ How we will make the test fair.
- ▲ What we will need to measure.
- ▲ How we will record our results.

When planning and organising are complete, and the groups have prepared the equipment, pour an equal amount of hot water into the cups for all the groups. The children will need to take the temperature as soon as possible, and again at five-minute intervals. This information can be entered on to a prepared chart like that shown in Figure 2. Where necessary, help the children to read the thermometers and check that they are writing down their measurements correctly.

When all the water has cooled down to room temperature, the testing is over. Discuss the results as a class. Which material proved to be the best insulator? Which was the poorest insulator? Did the poorest insulator still keep the water warmer longer than the uncovered cup? Did groups using the same material get the same results? If not, what could be the reason for this? Were there any problems? Is it necessary to try any part of the test again? Give the children the opportunity to record their results and conclusions. Encourage them to record what they have found out from their results, if the results were what they expected, and any problems they encountered. Results can be presented in the form of a graph.

Likely problems

Children will need the confidence to read the thermometer scale quickly and at the right time; any lost readings will affect the result. The insulating material should be packed as evenly as possible, but not too tightly.

Concepts likely to emerge

Heat can be prevented from escaping by certain materials; these materials are good thermal insulators. Some materials are better thermal insulators than others.

Using the activity for assessment

All aspects of Experimental and Investigative Science are covered. Groups or individuals could be assessed on their ability to make careful observations and measurements and to draw conclusions from the results collected.

Other investigations

- ▲ Which cup is made of the best material for keeping a drink warm?
- ▲ Does a tea-cosy really work?
- ▲ Which pair of gloves is the best for keeping hands warm?

MELTING ICE

Previous skills/knowledge needed

Children will already have explored ice and watched it melt, but may not have considered the factors which cause ice to melt.

Key background information

Children are always fascinated by ice. They are especially interested in icebergs, their formation and the way they float and drift on the sea. Growing concern about melting ice-caps and the fate of Antarctica will add to their awareness. In Iceland, some icebergs are shed from glaciers into freshwater lakes. Plans to tow icebergs to drought-stricken parts of the world to supply fresh water are occasionally aired. The danger icebergs present to shipping is well known, particularly the story of the *Titanic*.

Preparation

Make enough ice-cubes for each group to have five, and keep them in a freezer or vacuum flask until required. Put some plastic bottles of water in a refrigerator to provide a supply of chilled water.

Resources needed

A supply of ice-cubes which are all approximately the same size; transparent beakers or other containers; salt; thermometers and stopwatches if required. A collection of pictures and books about the cold regions of the Earth, showing the formation and melting of icebergs.

What to do

Before introducing the activity, prepare a display of material

about ice and especially icebergs to create interest and provide points for discussion. Then talk to the whole class about ice melting and find out what the children know about icebergs. Ask which factors they think might be involved in influencing the rate at which ice melts. Discuss the different conditions in which ice is found, such as floating in salt water (chunks of glaciers breaking off into the sea), floating in fresh water (glaciers breaking off into freshwater lagoons), or melting surrounded only by air. Consider also the temperature of the water in which the ice is melting.

Ask if the children can think of a way of testing the different rates at which ice melts. Can they create similar situations to those given above for observation in the classroom? What could represent the icebergs? Ideas will probably involve using ice-cubes. How many different situations will be tested? What will these be? Talk about using amounts of tap water and

Name:				Date:	
Melting ice					
Ice melting	Ice in chilled tap water	Ice in chilled salt water	Ice in room-temperature tap water	Ice in room-temperature salt water	Ice in air
After 5 minutes					
After 10 minutes					
After 15 minutes					
After 20 minutes					
After 25 minutes					
After 30 minutes					

Figure 3

MATERIALS

salt water in which to float the ice. Should the temperature of the water used be considered? Most icebergs will be floating in very cold water, but some will drift into warmer currents. Ice melting in the air can be included in the test.

Children should consider how to make the test fair. In their groups, encourage them to discuss and plan the organisation of their ideas. Headings to guide the children in their recording could include:

▲ What we want to find out.
▲ How we will do this.
▲ The equipment we will use.
▲ What we think will happen.
▲ How we will make sure that the test is fair.

While planning is in progress, assist groups where necessary. Make sure that they have decided upon a workable investigation using suitable equipment. Small transparent containers are ideal for each test. Ice could be tested in up to five different ways, such as in very cold tap water, in room- temperature tap water, in very cold salt water, in room-temperature salt water, and in an empty container. Ask which factors will need to be kept the same (the amount of water in which the ice floats, the moment each ice-cube is put in the water, the position and treatment of the ice during the test, and the position of the container). Ask the groups to predict what will happen and to make sure they know what they will be looking for. How will they collect evidence? Will timing be necessary or will they rely on observation alone? One group might be interested to measure

the temperatures in the containers, in which case they will need a thermometer for each one.

When each group has discussed, planned, organised an efficient working strategy and recorded their plan, they can carry out the test. Check that the equipment is ready to receive the ice, so that the test under each condition remains as fair as possible. While they are waiting and observing, the children can draw and annotate what is happening to the ice in each container, pointing out the factors which are different. A chart can also be prepared to record the results. (See Figure 3.) Children can make observations and comments at five-minute intervals; but adjust this time according to the temperature of the room and how quickly you think the ice will melt.

Talk to each group as the test proceeds. Ask the children to tell you the progress of the melting so far. Which ice-cube has melted the most? Is this what they expected? Point out that touching, stirring or even breathing on any of the containers could affect the melting and make the test unfair. Check that the children record their observations accurately. They could highlight the comments for the ice-cube which seems to be melting the fastest.

After all the testing is complete, compare the results of all the groups. How are they similar? Did every group get the same result? If so, what does this tell us? Did the findings of the groups contradict each other? If so, could there be a reason for this? Were any of the predictions proved correct? Did anything unexpected happen? Is there anything which is difficult to explain? Encourage children to draw conclusions while appreciating the limitations of their test. A bar graph can be drawn to show the time taken for the ice-cubes to melt under each condition.

Likely problems

It could be difficult convincing the children that all the ice-cubes used for their test are the same size. To overcome this problem, try using ice 'cube' bags (available from most supermarkets) which produce more even-sized shapes and make handling simpler. Efficiency is required to transfer the ice-cubes to the test without any melting. A cool box is useful and can store the ice close to where it is required.

Some children might find it difficult to judge which ice-cube is melting the fastest. Show them how to compare by glancing at one and then another, seeing how near to the edge of the container they are and how much is below the water level. (Do these factors affect the rate of melting?) Encourage their confidence in their own suggestions and decisions.

Organise this investigation so that the children will not be interrupted; it is important that time should be available to complete the testing.

Concepts likely to emerge

The rate at which ice melts is influenced by its surroundings;

MATERIALS

ice in water will melt more rapidly than ice in air. An increase in the temperature of the surrounding water will cause the rate of melting to increase. Ice in salt water melts less quickly than ice in fresh water.

Using the activity for assessment

Except for checking observations and measurements by repeating the process, all aspects of Experimental and Investigative Science are covered by this investigation. By talking to individual children as well as reading and discussing their records, it is possible to assess a child's skill in planning and carrying out an investigation.

Other investigations

▲ Does the size of the piece of ice affect the rate at which it melts?

▲ Does the amount of water have any effect on the melting of ice?

FREEZING LIQUIDS

Do some liquids freeze more quickly than others?

Children working in groups of four or five.

50–60 minutes for discussing, planning and recording; at least one hour for observation; 20 minutes for drawing conclusions and final recording.

Previous skills/knowledge needed

Children will need to have experimented with the processes of freezing and melting water, and will perhaps have raised further questions about the behaviour of other liquids as they are cooled below 0°C.

Key background information

As liquids cool, their molecules become less mobile. Instead of sliding over each other they form regimented groups, and the liquid begins to take on a solid form. The temperature at which this happens depends on the molecular structure of the liquid. Pure water freezes at 0°C.

Preparation

Make sure that freezing space is available. Collect a selection of liquids for testing such as tap water, salt water, fruit juice, vinegar, milk, cooking oil.

Resources needed

A freezing facility; small plastic or aluminium foil containers to hold liquids; a plastic plate or small tray for each group.

What to do

Prompt the children to remind each other of what happens to water as it cools. They will say that when the temperature reaches 0°C, water starts to freeze. Ask if they think this is what happens to other liquids. Explain that you want them to find out if other liquids freeze in the same way as water. Ask the children to suggest liquids which could be safely tested. Suitable liquids include milk, fruit juice, cooking oil, vinegar and salt water. Show the children the freezing facility they are to use, and how much space is available. Ask what sort of containers would be suitable for the experiment. Is it possible to devise a fair test? What will need to be kept the same? What will be different in each case? The children should realise that the amount of liquid to be tested should be constant and identical containers should be used, the variable factor being the liquid. As far as is possible, the containers should be placed close together without touching in the freezer to receive the same conditions. Small containers placed on a tray or plastic plate can easily be

Name:				Date:	
Liquids to be tested					
After 10 minutes					
After 20 minutes					
After 30 minutes					
After 40 minutes					
After 50 minutes					
After 60 minutes					

Figure 4

removed for observation. Ask when would be the best time to start the freezing so that the maximum number of observations can be carried out. Small amounts of liquid placed in a freezer will soon start to freeze, and up to two hours will be needed for frequent observations.

Give the children the opportunity to discuss their plan as a group, organise their working strategy and record it before starting. Headings to guide recording might include:
▲ What we want to find out.
▲ What we think will happen.
▲ How we will carry out our investigation.
▲ What equipment we will use.
▲ How we will make the test fair.
▲ What we will need to measure.
▲ How we will record our results.

During the planning, talk to the children about preparing a chart to collect their results. (See Figure 4.) Ask how often they will look at the liquids, and what problems could arise if the liquids are frequently removed from the freezer. Suggest observations every 10 minutes and prepare the chart accordingly.

As the children carry out the test, check that they measure the liquids, either in spoonfuls or using a millilitre measure. Try to be present when observations are being made, to check that children are examining and describing accurately. After they have made an initial visual comparison, a skewer can be used to probe the liquids gently in order to ascertain how the freezing process has progressed.

Note down the children's comments and observations to save time (these can be written on the board for recording while awaiting the next observation time). Questions to ask could include: Do the liquids look any different? Has the colour of any of them changed? Are there signs of freezing? What do these signs look like? Is it possible to order the liquids

according to how much freezing has taken place as the experiment progresses?

When testing and observations are complete, ask the children what they have found out. Do some liquids freeze more quickly than others? Which was the first liquid to freeze? Was this what they expected? Did all the liquids freeze at different times? Which liquid took the longest time to freeze? These questions can help with drawing conclusions.

Likely problems
If freezing facilities are limited, it might not be possible for all the groups to investigate at the same time. Observations will need to be made quite quickly before the liquids begin to melt.

Concepts likely to emerge
Different liquids behave differently when temperatures fall below their freezing points. Pure water freezes quickly; water containing other materials, such as salt water, vinegar and milk, will take longer to freeze.

Using the activity for assessment
All aspects of Experimental and Investigative Science are covered by this investigation. As many children as possible can be assessed on one area, or a group of children can be assessed on all areas.

HEATING AND DISSOLVING

Does the temperature of water affect how much of a material will dissolve in it?
†† *Children working in pairs or small groups.*
🕐 *One hour for discussion, planning and recording; 45 minutes for testing, recording and concluding.*
⚠ *Children should be warned not to taste solutions and to take care with hot liquids.*

Previous skills/knowledge needed
Children will need to have explored the process of dissolving and understand that there is a limit to the amount of a solid soluble material that will dissolve in a given amount of water. They should know the meaning of the term 'saturated solution'.

Key background information
When no further soluble material will dissolve in a liquid, the solution has become saturated. If the solution is warmed, it will be able to dissolve even more of the material. Children can stir a soluble material into two containers, one with warm water and the other with chilled water, to see which is the first to become a saturated solution.

Preparation

Chill some water in a refrigerator; make ice-cubes.

Resources needed

Two small transparent containers per group; spoons; soluble materials such as sugar, salt, bath salts, and so on; chilled water; ice-cubes.

What to do

Prompt the children to remind each other what is meant by a 'saturated solution'. Ask them to tell you how they would produce a saturated solution using sugar (or another soluble material) and water. Can they think of anything which might cause the amount of soluble material needed to make a saturated solution to change? What happens when sugar is added to hot and cold drinks?

Tell the children that you would like them to find out if the temperature of water has any effect on the amount of a soluble material needed to make a saturated solution. Will a different amount of soluble material dissolve in hot water than will dissolve in cold water? Ask for suggestions as to how this could be tested. How will the temperature of the water be changed? What things will be compared? Suggestions might include using very cold water and very warm water. What will the problems be in testing this? How can the temperatures of the water be maintained in each case? (Chilled water from the refrigerator can be used and the container can be surrounded by ice while the test proceeds. Very warm water can be used *with care* and the container can be surrounded by an insulating material.) This part of the test will need to be carried out as quickly as possible.

Allow the groups time to plan, organise and record their intentions. Encourage an efficient method of working. Will the two liquids be investigated at the same time? How much of the soluble material will be added each time? What will they need to measure? How will the children remember the amounts added? How will they make sure the test is fair? How will they know when the solution has become saturated? When will the investigation be over? Headings to help with recording could include:

▲ What we want to find out.
▲ What we think will happen.
▲ How we will carry out our investigation.
▲ What equipment we will use.
▲ How we will make the test fair.
▲ What we will need to measure amounts.
▲ How we will record our results.

When the children are ready, provide the very warm water and the chilled water in the right amounts. The children should begin by adding the first spoonful of the soluble material to each sample of water and stirring. After each spoonful, the children should check whether all the material has dissolved or not. As each solution becomes saturated, the children should stop adding more material to it and conclusions can be drawn. Was there a difference between the amounts of soluble material which were added to the warm water and the cold water? Is this what was expected? Were there any problems to overcome while doing this test? How successful was the test? Would it be helpful to repeat the test? Encourage the children to present their results, and help them to formulate a conclusion.

Likely problems

The test must be performed quite quickly before the temperatures of the water samples change, so the children need to be thoroughly prepared and to work efficiently.

Concepts likely to emerge

If equal amounts of soluble material is added to equal amounts of warm and cold water, more will dissolve in the warm water.

Using the activity for assessment

All aspects of Experimental and Investigative Science can be covered by this investigation. Children can be assessed on their ability to use equipment efficiently, make careful observations and draw conclusions.

Assessment

This section contains a selection of activities which you can use for summative assessment purposes. The activities have been designed to be used in two ways. Firstly, the individual tasks can provide you with ongoing feedback on children's progress. Secondly, all the activities could be presented together as a form of summative assessment at the end of a whole unit on one of the five topics covered, or at the end of Key Stage 2. The activities for each topic do not have to be attempted in any particular order. They are numbered only to aid cross-referencing.

All the activities presented in this section require similar classroom organisation, preparation, resources and information about what to do. Information about the PoS to be addressed, likely outcomes and reinforcement suggestions are provided separately for each activity. The activities provide a form of summative assessment which will assist in determining individual children's overall level of achievement. It will also enable you to assess those areas which may need reinforcement work, and will thus help to determine future planning requirements.

Used in conjunction with the formative assessment activities outlined in the main chapters, these activities will help you to provide feedback on progress to children and parents, as well as helping you to decide where to go next in planning for the children's learning. The completed activities could also be kept as part of a pupil profile to assist each child's current, or subsequent, teacher in determining starting-points for individual pupil planning.

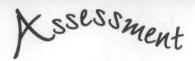
CLASSIFYING MATERIALS

ACTIVITY 1
PoS to be addressed
To identify a range of common materials.
Likely outcome
Answers: nail – metal; milk bottle – glass; sock – fabric; brick – clay; magazine – paper; fence – wood; cubes – plastic; ball – rubber.
Reinforcement suggestions
Provide a selection of familiar items which can be sorted into groups according to the material from which they are made.

ACTIVITY 2
PoS to be addressed
To compare everyday materials on the basis of their properties.
Likely outcome
Answers: rock – hard, strong; spring – strong, flexible; vase – transparent, breakable; scissors – hard, strong; plank of wood – hard, strong; plastic bag – flexible, strong, transparent; T-shirt – flexible, strong; tyre – strong, flexible.
Reinforcement suggestions
Provide a selection of items and ask the children to describe their properties.

ACTIVITY 3
PoS to be addressed
To relate properties of materials to their everyday uses.
Likely outcome
Answers: copper wire – conducts electricity, strong, flexible; plastic hose-pipe – strong, waterproof, flexible; window glass – transparent, waterproof, hard, strong; steel girders – strong, hard; paving stones – hard, durable; wooden furniture – strong, attractive; woollen clothing – thermal insulator, attractive; iron magnet – magnetic, strong, hard.
Reinforcement suggestions
Examine items in the room and decide why they were made from those particular materials.

ACTIVITY 4
PoS to be addressed
To compare everyday materials according to their magnetic behaviour.
Likely outcome
Answers: scissors, paper-clip and nail are magnetic.
Reinforcement suggestions
Give the children further opportunity to test a variety of materials with a magnet.

ACTIVITY 5
PoS to be addressed
Some materials are better thermal insulators than others.
Likely outcome
A wooden spoon is a poor conductor of heat, and therefore the handle remains cool while stirring hot food; a plastic handle remains cool and prevents heat reaching the hand while the metal saucepan is very hot; a tea cosy prevents the heat escaping too quickly from the hot tea; carpets stop heat from escaping through the floor, and since they hold on to heat they feel warm.
Reinforcement suggestions
Children can carry out further tests on insulating materials; in cold weather, they can find ways to prevent heat escaping from their bodies.

ACTIVITY 6
PoS to be addressed
Some materials are better electrical conductors than others.
Likely outcome
Copper, brass and steel are good electrical conductors.
Reinforcement suggestions
Children can carry out further tests to discover which materials are the best electrical conductors.

ACTIVITY 7
PoS to be addressed
To describe rocks according to their characteristics, including appearance, texture and permeability.
Likely outcome
Common rocks the children may know include chalk, limestone, sandstone and slate.
Reinforcement suggestions
Two children can each be given a different rock and take turns to describe a characteristic of their rock.

ACTIVITY 8
PoS to be addressed
To describe soils according to their characteristics, including appearance, texture and permeability.
Likely outcome
Types of soil the children may be familiar with include sandy and clay soils.
Reinforcement suggestions
Two children can each be given a different soil sample and take turns to describe a characteristic of their soil.

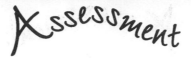

ACTIVITY 9

PoS to be addressed

To recognise differences between solids, liquids and gases.

Likely outcome

Solids – dustbin, brick, sun-hat, glass jar; liquids – milk, blood, petrol, cooking oil; gases – oxygen, smoke, car exhaust fumes, carbon dioxide.

Reinforcement suggestions

Collect examples and pictures of solids, liquids and gases for children to practise sorting.

ACTIVITY 10

PoS to be addressed

To recognise differences between solids, liquids and gases in terms of ease of flow and maintenance of shape and volume.

Likely outcome

Answers: balloon – gas; suitcase – solids; bottle – liquids, possibly gas if children are thinking about fizzy drinks; basket – solids; pipe – liquids and gases; bucket – liquids and solids; oxygen cylinders – gas; box – solids.

Reinforcement suggestions

Children can make collections of containers for each of these types of material; solids and liquids will be quite easy, but they will begin to realise how difficult it is to contain a gas.

ACTIVITY 11

PoS to be addressed

To recognise differences between solids, liquids and gases in terms of ease of flow and maintenance of shape and volume.

Likely outcome

A solid is easily held in the hand and has a definite shape; a liquid has no shape of its own, finds its own level and flows easily through a pipe; a gas has no shape of its own, spreads out in all directions, flows easily through a pipe and can be squashed into a smaller volume.

Reinforcement suggestions

Children can consider how solids, liquids and gases are moved about as they are needed; a list can be made of the problems involved.

ACTIVITY 12

PoS to be addressed

To recognise differences between solids, liquids and gases in terms of ease of flow and maintenance of shape and volume.

Likely outcome

Picture 1: solid – sides of fish tank, liquid – water, gas – bubbles of air; picture 2: solid – bottle, liquid – drink, gas – bubbles of carbon dioxide; picture 3: solid – bath, liquid – water (and dissolved soap), gas – bubbles of air (trapped in soap solution); picture 4: solid – candles and cake (and smoke particles), liquid – melted wax, gas – gases from burning candle and air being blown to put out flame.

Reinforcement suggestions

Look around and discuss examples of solids, liquids and gases.

CHANGING MATERIALS

ACTIVITY 1

PoS to be addressed

Mixing materials can cause them to change; heating or cooling materials can cause them to change; some changes can be reversed and some cannot; melting, boiling, freezing and evaporating are changes that can be reversed; changes that occur when materials are burned are not reversible.

Likely outcome

Baking – dough – hardens – not reversible; freezing – water – becomes solid – reversible; melting – chocolate – softens, becomes liquid – reversible; burning – wood – charcoal remains, gases escape into atmosphere – not reversible; boiling – water – evaporates into air – reversible; mixing – salt and water – a solution is formed – reversible; evaporating – water – becomes part of the atmosphere – reversible; burning – wax – melts and eventually burns away, with gases becoming part of the atmosphere – not reversible; baking – clay – becomes hard – not reversible; melting – ice – becomes water – reversible; mixing – sand and water – a mixture is formed – reversible; burning – paper – ash and gases are formed – not reversible.

Reinforcement suggestions

Children will need to explore further those processes with which they still have difficulty.

ACTIVITY 2

PoS to be addressed

Temperature is a measure of how hot or cold materials are.

Likely outcome

Water boils at 100°C; water freezes at 0°C; the usual classroom temperature is about 18°C; the temperature inside a freezer is about –20°C, and that inside a refrigerator between 1°C and 7°C.

Reinforcement suggestions

Encourage children to read the temperature measurement on a thermometer in different locations to familiarise themselves with the scale and relative temperatures.

ACTIVITY 3

PoS to be addressed

Dissolving, melting, boiling, condensing, freezing and evaporating are changes that can be reversed.

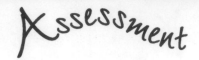

Likely outcome

Answers: kettle – boiling; water vapour – condensing on window; food in freezer – freezing; ice-cream – melting; water – evaporating from bowl; sugar – being dissolved in tea.

Reinforcement suggestions

Children can explore further those processes with which they are unsure.

ACTIVITY 4

PoS to be addressed

Melting, boiling, condensing, freezing and evaporating are changes that can be reversed.

Likely outcome

Saucepan of water boiling – water evaporates into air, becomes water vapour, meets the cooler temperature of the window pane, condenses to form water; washing line – water evaporates from washing, becomes water vapour in the air, condenses into drops of water on meeting cooler air, forms clouds, falls as rain; snow melting – snow melts and turns to water, drips from roof, freezes as icicles, melts again, freezes on ground and finally melts.

Reinforcement suggestions

Children can observe boiling and condensation processes again, and explore the freezing and melting cycle further.

ACTIVITY 5

PoS to be addressed

The water cycle and the roles of evaporation and condensation.

Likely outcome

Correct order: rain falls on land; water drains into rivers; rivers flow into the sea; water evaporates from the sea; water vapour rises into the air; cooler air causes condensation; clouds are formed.

Reinforcement suggestions

Cut out the sentences and let two children invent a game that involves ordering the stages of the water cycle.

⬡ SEPARATING MIXTURES

PoS to be addressed

Solid particles of different sizes can be separated by sieving.

Likely outcome

Children should describe how they would use an appropriate type of sieve and containers to separate and collect the ingredients of the mixture.

Reinforcement suggestions

Give children further opportunity to try the sieving process.

ACTIVITY 2

PoS to be addressed

Some solids dissolve in water to make solutions but some do not.

Likely outcome

Bath salts, sugar and salt are soluble and sand, chalk, flour and talcum powder are insoluble (in cold water).

Reinforcement suggestions

Children can test these materials to see if they dissolve in water or not.

ACTIVITY 3

PoS to be addressed

Some solids dissolve in water to give a solution. A material which dissolves in water will seem to disappear. The water will be clear (although the colour may change) and there will be no sediment in the bottom.

Reinforcement suggestions

Children should dissolve a soluble material in water and examine the solution.

ACTIVITY 4

PoS to be addressed

Insoluble solids can be separated from liquids by filtering.

Likely outcomes

Children should explain how to filter the water to remove the particles of mud.

Reinforcement suggestions

Allow children to practise the filtering process.

ACTIVITY 5

PoS to be addressed

Solids that have dissolved can be recovered by evaporating the liquid from the solution.

Likely outcome

Children should describe how the water will be evaporated, leaving the salt behind.

Reinforcement activities

Allow children to carry out this activity for themselves.

ACTIVITY 6

PoS to be addressed

There is a limit to the mass of solid that can dissolve in a given amount of water.

Likely outcome

Children should describe how a soluble material is added to a liquid until no more will dissolve.

Reinforcement suggestions

Allow the children to make a saturated solution. Can they think of any factors which might affect how much of a given solid can dissolve in a given amount of water?

Photocopiables

The pages in this section can be photocopied for use in the classroom or school which has purchased this book, and do not need to be declared in any return in respect of any photocopying licence.

They comprise a varied selection of both pupil and teacher resources, including pupil worksheets, resource material and record sheets to be completed by the teacher or children. Most of the photocopiable pages are related to individual activities in the book; the name of the activity is indicated at the top of the sheet, together with a page reference indicating where the lesson plan for that activity can be found.

Individual pages are discussed in detail within each lesson plan, accompanied by ideas for adaptation where appropriate – of course, each sheet can be adapted to suit your own needs and those of your class. Sheets can also be coloured, laminated, mounted on to card, enlarged, and so on where appropriate.

Pupil worksheets and record sheets have spaces provided for children's names and for noting the date on which each sheet was used. This means that, if so required, they can be included easily within any pupil assessment portfolio.

The activities on pages 138 to 157 can be used for the purposes of summative assessment. Background notes for these activities are provided in the Assessment chapter.

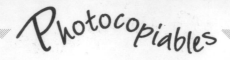

Sorting materials, see page 14

What are things made of?

Name _____   Date _____

▲ Sort your objects according to the materials from which they are made.

Wood

Metal

Paper

Plastic

Fabric

Rocks

Things I am not sure about

MATERIALS

Sorting materials, see page 14

Sorting materials

metal	rubber	plastic	fabric
wood	rocks	glass	paper

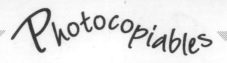
Describing materials

Name _____   Date _____

Material	These words describe the material
metal	
plastic	
paper	
wood	
fabric	
rock	
rubber	
glass	

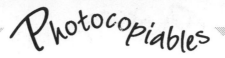

Testing for hardness

Name _____ Date _____

Which materials are you testing?	Which tools are you using?

◇ What is your plan?

◇ Use this chart to show your results. Use ticks to show which tools scratched each material.

Tools

Materials					

◇ Which tool scratched the most materials?
◇ Which material was marked by the most tools?
◇ Which material is the softest?
◇ Which material is the hardest?
◇ List the materials starting with the softest and ending with the hardest.

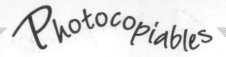

Testing for hardness

Name _____   Date _____

▲ Record the results of your scratch test below.

<table>
<tr>
<td>

These things were
scratched by a twig
(wood).

</td>
<td>

These things were
scratched by a nail
(metal).

</td>
</tr>
<tr>
<td>

These things were
scratched by a stone
(rock).

</td>
<td>

These things were
scratched by a pen
(plastic).

</td>
</tr>
</table>

▲ Which tool scratched the most things?
▲ Which material is the hardest?

MATERIALS

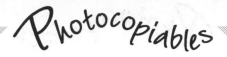

Strong or stronger, see page 19

Testing for strength

Name _____   **Date** _____

What we want to find out.

What we are using.

This is our prediction of the order of strength.

Test one	Test two
This is what we will do.	This is what we will do.
Our results:	Our results:

▲ Which paper have you decided is the strongest?
▲ Which paper have you decided is the least strong?
▲ Is this what you expected?

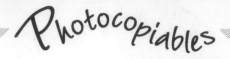

Looking for strength

Name _____   Date _____

Wood can be strong.	Plastic can be strong.
Metal can be strong.	Fabric can be strong.

▲ Draw other examples of strong materials you have found on the back of this sheet.

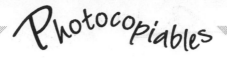

Being flexible, see page 21

Flexibility

Name _____   Date _____

Flexible means

_____

_____

▲ Write down the names of flexible things you have found.

_____

_____

Some things might be more flexible than others.
▲ Sort your list into groups according to how flexible they are.

slightly flexible	quite flexible	very flexible

▲ Rearrange your list into groups according to the material they are made of.

metal	plastic	wood	fabric	rubber	paper

Many flexible things are made of _____ .
Very few flexible things are made of _____ .

Floating and sinking, see page 22

Floating and sinking

Name _____ Date _____

▲ Which things will float and which will sink?

Things we are testing	My predictions: will float/will sink/not sure		My observations	My comments

MATERIALS

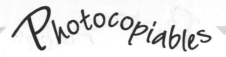

Soaking up water, see page 23

Soaking up water

Name _____ Date _____

What we are going to find out:

This is a piece of the material we are testing.

This is what the material looks like through a hand-lens.

How we will carry out the plan:

What we will be looking for:

What we must be careful about to make our test work well:

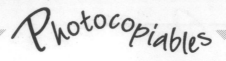
Testing materials with magnets

Name _____   Date _____

▲ Draw or write down the names of about 20 items.

Sort the items into two groups.

Those you think the magnet will pull.	Those you think the magnet will not pull.

▲ Now test the items with your magnet and make new lists.

These are magnetic:	These are non-magnetic:

▲ What are the items in the magnetic group made of?

▲ Mix together a handful of paper-clips with a handful of plastic counters. What is the best way of separating them? Explain what you did on the back of this sheet.

Photocopiables

Escaping heat, see page 26

Escaping heat

Name _____   Date _____

Season: _____   Weather conditions: _____

Outside temperature: _____   Inside temperature: _____

I have just been ..... _____

These things are cooler than my hands:	My hands feel: cold cool warm hot	These things are warmer than my hands:

Ideas for keeping myself cool:	Ideas for keeping myself warm:

▲ Finish off these sentences.

Heat is always trying to _____ .

Heat moves from a _____ material to a cold _____ .

▲ Draw in arrowheads to show which way the heat is escaping.

radiator   frozen peas   hot chocolate   ice cubes

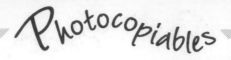
Holding on to heat

Name _____   Date _____

What are we trying to find out?

What is our plan?

How will we know if the items have kept some of their heat?

Items we are testing	How they feel after the test			
	Slightly cold	Cold	Very cold	Comments

The materials which are the best insulators of heat are _____.

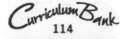
MATERIALS

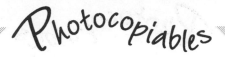
Thermal insulators in the kitchen, see page 32

Thermal insulators in the kitchen

▲ Find examples of thermal insulation in this picture.

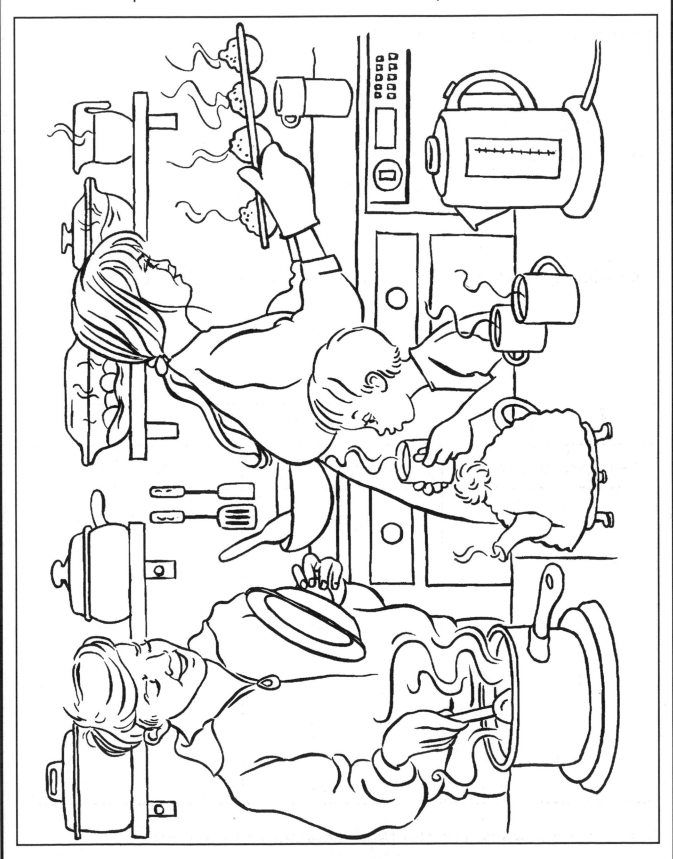

Keeping warm

Name _____   Date _____

▲ Look closely at some fabrics using a hand-lens and draw the fibres.

Fabrics for winter clothes

Fabrics for summer clothes

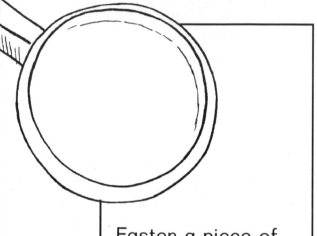

Fasten a piece of winter fabric here.

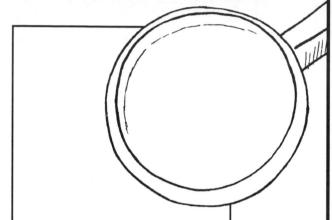

Fasten a piece of summer fabric here.

Fasten a piece of winter fabric here.

Fasten a piece of summer fabric here.

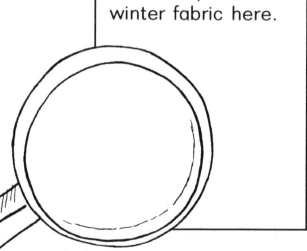

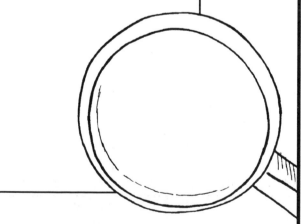

▲ Describe the fabrics which keep us warm.

▲ Describe the fabrics which keep us cool.

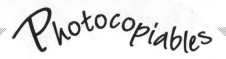

Materials conducting electricity, see page 34

Testing electrical conductors

Name _____   Date _____

▲ Draw your circuit here.

Things we tested:	Is the bulb bright?	Is the bulb dim?	Does the bulb stay unlit?

We have discovered that materials which are good conductors of electricity are _____

We have discovered that materials which are bad conductors of electricity are _____

Choosing the right material, see page 37

Which material is best?

Name _____   Date _____

▲ Which materials would be best to make the things on the left?

▲ Circle your choice.   ▲ Give your reasons.

A bird table	paper sponge wood	glass rubber metal	
A pencil case	stone tissue-paper metal	plastic glass wood	
A fireguard	paper plastic card	wood metal fabric	
An envelope	rubber metal glass	wood wool paper	
A dog's waterproof coat	sponge metal wool	plastic paper wood	

Choosing the right material, see page 37

Long-lasting materials

Name _____   Date _____

Material	Is it natural or man-made?	Is it durable?	Can it be recycled?	Is it biodegradable?	Is the source renewable or limited?
plastic					
paper					
wood					
glass					
rubber					
metal					

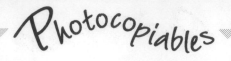
A close look at rocks, see page 38

A close look at rocks

▲ Examine your rock samples very carefully. These words might help you to describe the appearance and texture of each rock.

rough   smooth   sharp   edges   firm

holes   grains   fossils   crystals   soft   hard   shiny

Draw the rock	Describe the colour	Describe the appearance	Describe the texture

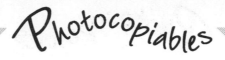
A close look at rocks, see page 38

Our classroom rocks

Name _____ Date _____

Does it have any holes?	
Is it shiny or dull?	
Are there any crystals?	
Can you see fossils?	
Is it rough or smooth?	
Draw and colour each rock.	

 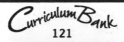

Looking closely at soils, see page 41

Examining soils

Name _____   Date _____

Soils	Rub a small amount between your finger and thumb. How does it feel?	Take a small amount and roll it in the palm of your hand. Does it make a ball?	Look at it with a hand-lens and describe its appearance.	Look closely and describe the colour.
My soil sample				
My partner's soil sample				
Mystery sample A				
Mystery sample B				

MATERIALS

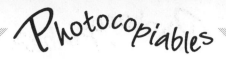
Looking closely at soils

Name _____   Date _____

The soil is ...	My soil	My partner's soil
black		
brown		
greyish		
reddish		
yellowish		
wet		
dry		
lumpy		
grainy		
gritty		
stony		
smooth		
able to be moulded into a ball		
A sample of the soil		

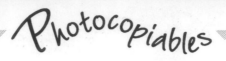
Solid, liquid or gas

Name _____   Date _____

▲ Use three different colours to fill in the boxes on the right. Now look at the pictures below and colour in the corners of the boxes according to your key.

solid	liquid	gas

MATERIALS

Warming air, see page 48

Detecting air currents

Name _____ Date _____

▲ Make a spiral snake to detect rising air.

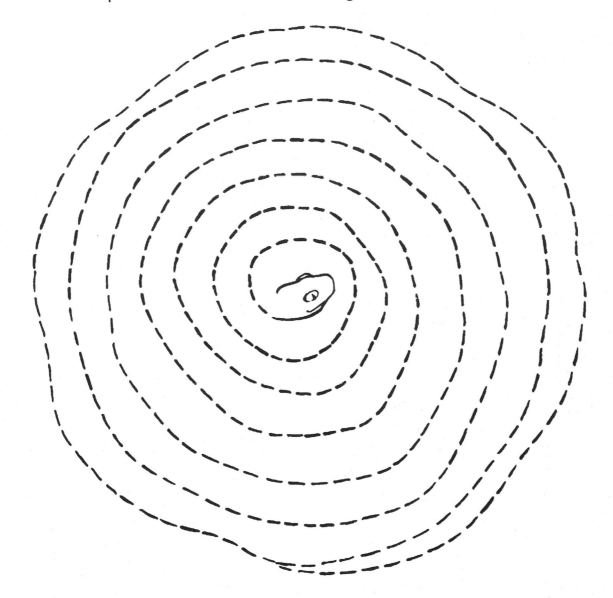

▲ Colour in the snake, then cut it out and cut along the dotted line. Colour in the other side of your snake.

▲ Tie a knot at the end of a piece of thin thread. Thread this on to a needle, and pierce a hole through the eye of the snake. Draw the thread through.

▲ Ask for help to hang your snake where you think there is hot air rising.

▲ What happens?

Bubbles, see page 50

Bubbles

Name _____   Date _____

Bubbles are _____

_____

▲ Draw the bubbles in these pictures. The last two are for your own examples.

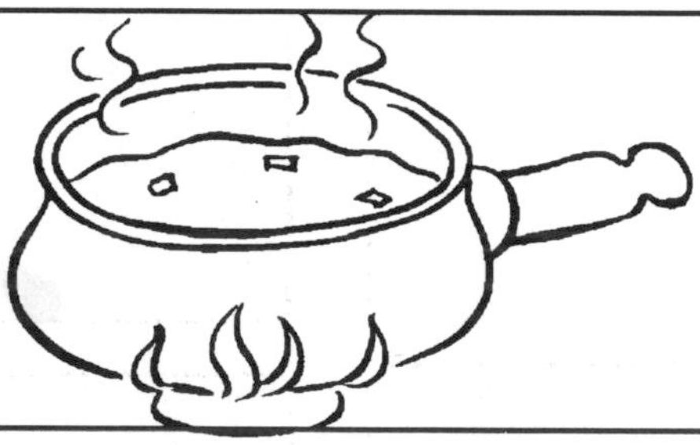

▲ Draw your glass of fizzy drink.

The bubbles in the fizzy drink are

_____

▲ Describe what is happening to the bubbles in the drink.

_____

_____

▲ Why do the bubbles rise to the surface?

▲ What has happened when the drink has gone flat?

▲ How long did it take for the glass of fizzy drink to lose all its bubbles?

MATERIALS

Heating solid materials, see page 55

Heating solid materials

Name _____   Date _____

▲ Record your observations on the chart below.

A sketch of the material	The name of the material we are testing	A description of the material before heating	Observations and comments

▲ Use these boxes to group and label your materials according to what happened to them when they were heated.

Below zero

Name _____   Date _____

What do we want to find out?

How will we carry out the test?

What do we think will happen?

Materials we are testing	A description of the material at room temperature	Comments on the materials after they have been in the freezer

▲ Use these boxes to group and label the materials after cooling.

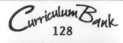

MATERIALS

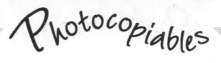

Feeling hot, feeling cold, see page 59

Feeling hot, feeling cold

Name _____ Date _____

▲ These words describe different temperatures. Look at the pictures below. Decide which description is the best for each picture. Write the words in the spaces below each picture.

very hot   hot   warm   cool   cold   very cold

Make a thermometer

Cut along lines like this - - - - -

Fold along lines like this ———

C ——— C

▲ Cut along the dotted lines. (Do not lose this piece of paper.)

▲ Fold carefully along line A and then along line B.

▲ Colour the reverse side of the piece of paper between lines A and B in red.

▲ Glue the reverse side of the flap on the left, then fold along line B and stick the flap down.

▲ Fold line C on this piece of paper. Use it to mark the temperature by slotting it inside your thermometer at the top.

0

B

B

Colour the other side of this section red.

A

A

Glue the other side of this flap.

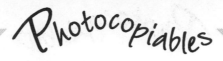
Measuring low temperatures

Name _____   **Date** _____

Today's temperature in the classroom is _____

Today's temperature outside the classroom is _____

▲ Complete the numbers of this scale.
▲ Write in any low temperatures you have measured.

Other low temperatures I have found out about.

0°C — Water freezes

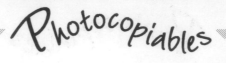

Evaporation is everywhere

Name _____   Date _____

Sometimes water evaporates quickly, sometimes more slowly.
▲ How do we know this?
▲ Write down some examples.

▲ What kind of a test could you do to prove this happens?

▲ What will you need to keep the same each time?

▲ What will be different?

▲ What were the results of your test?

▲ What do the results tell you?

MATERIALS

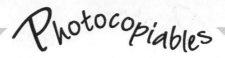
Evaporation in different liquids, see page 68

Do liquids evaporate at different rates?

Name _____   Date _____

▲ Record your observations on the chart below

	Liquid:	Liquid:	Liquid:	Liquid:
Day 1 Date:				
Day 2 Date:				
Day 3 Date:				
Day 4 Date:				

▲ Can you put the liquids in order according to how quickly they evaporated?

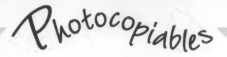

Mixing mystery materials

▲ Follow these instructions carefully.

1 Check you have everything you need. There is a checklist on your recording sheet.

2 Use a hand-lens to examine the mystery material. Describe what it looks like and stick a small sample to your recording sheet with sticky tape.

3 Stir one spoonful of the material into the water. Describe what happened.

4 Carefully pour the liquid into the flat dish and put it in a safe place. Make a label to identify your dish.

5 Write down what you think will happen to the liquid in the dish.

6 Wait for a day and look at the liquid again.

7 Describe what has happened.
Where is the water?
Where is the mystery material?
Does it look the same as before?
Examine it with a hand-lens.

8 On the back of your recording sheet draw the shapes you can see in the mystery material. What do you think the material might be?

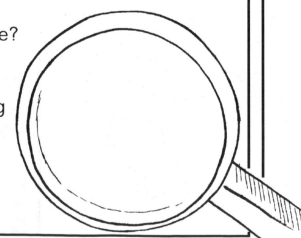

Mixing mystery materials, see page 69

Mixing mystery materials

Name _____   Date _____

Equipment check-list

a hand-lens
a container of water
a spoon
a flat dish
a label
a mystery material

▲ Describe the mystery material.

What we did.

What happened.

What we did next.

What we think will happen.

WAIT AND SEE!

What has happened?

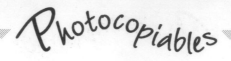
Condensation

Name _____ Date _____

Condensation is ...

Where I have seen examples of condensation.

At school	At home

▲ Now test some materials to find out if they cause condensation.

Our plan:

Materials	My prediction	Result

Boiling and condensing, see page 72

Boiling and condensing

Name _____   Date _____

What I already know about boiling.

What I already know about condensing.

▲ Draw lines from the words below to the part of the picture that they describe.

hot
cold
boiling
condensing
water
water vapour

▲ What do you know about steam?

▲ What happens when a saucepan of water is left on a hot stove?

▲ Describe what happens when a lid is put on a saucepan of boiling water.

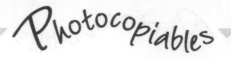
Rain falling on ...

▲ Cut out the cards below and order them to show how water might move during its movement in the water cycle.

makes a puddle on the playground	flows through pipes to school	is used to boil potatoes
falls on our house roof	evaporates	makes a trickle down our street
is emptied down drains	condenses in water vapour	falls on the garden
rushes down a drainpipe	soaks into my clothes	forms clouds
soaks into the ground	falls into a pond	rushes down drains
is cleaned at the water treatment works	runs into a stream	flows through pipes to my house
is used in a science investigation	is lapped up by a hedgehog	is taken up by tree roots
flows into a river	is drunk by me	flows into the sea

The water cycle, see page 73

The water cycle

Name _____   Date _____

▲ Write these words in the correct places on the picture.

evaporation   sea   land   river   rain   warm air
condensation   water vapour   clouds   cold air

▲ Draw arrows to show how water is moving to make the water cycle.

The water cycle, see page 73

The water cycle

Name _____   **Date** _____

This diagram shows the stages in the water cycle.

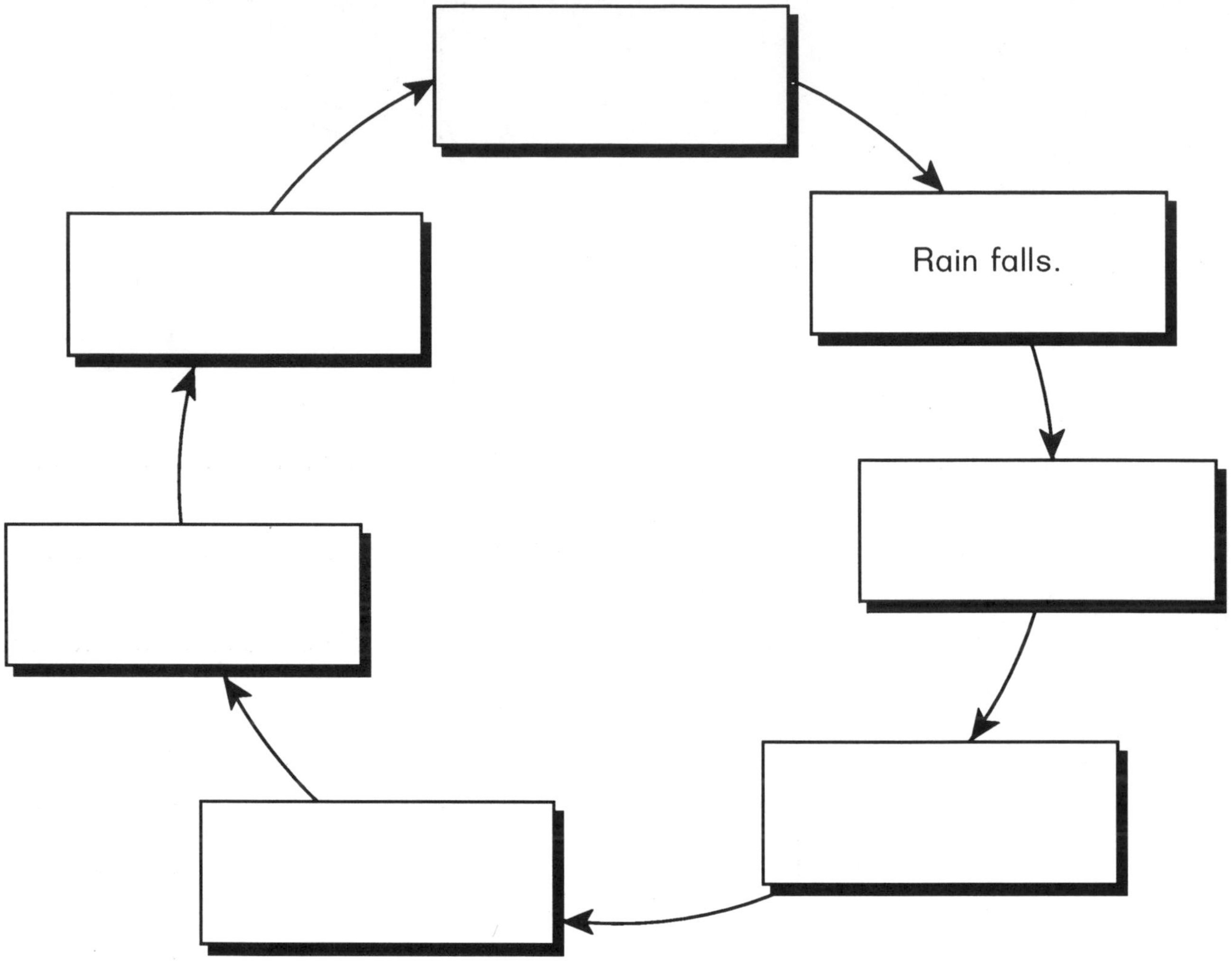

Rain falls.

▲ Write this information in the boxes in the correct order.

Water vapour evaporates into the air.	Water flows into a river.	Water drains through the ground.
Clouds form.	Water flows into the sea.	Condensation occurs and tiny water drops are formed.

▲ Put the symbol **W** to show where the air is warm in the cycle.
▲ Put the symbol **C** to show where the air is cool.

MATERIALS

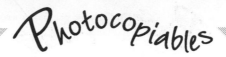
Making mixtures

Name _____   Date _____

▲ Draw a different mixture in each container. Give each one a name
and write how many different shapes and sizes of particle there are.

Name: _____

Number of shapes: _____

Number of sizes: _____

Name: _____

Number of shapes: _____

Number of sizes: _____

Name: _____

Number of shapes: _____

Number of sizes: _____

Name: _____

Number of shapes: _____

Number of sizes: _____

▲ Which mixture was the easiest to sort?
▲ Which mixture was the most difficult to sort?

MATERIALS

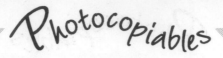
Mixing materials with water, see page 80

Mixing materials with water

Name _____   Date _____

A **soluble** material dissolves in water.
An **insoluble** material does not dissolve in water.
▲ Use these drawings to show what happens when each type of material is mixed with water. Describe what happens in each jar.

Soluble material

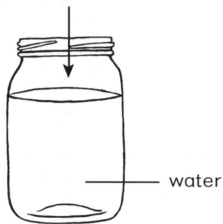

water

Insoluble material

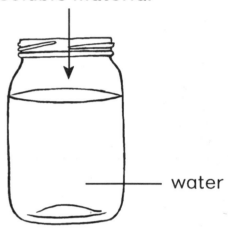

water

_____   _____

_____   _____

_____   _____

▲ Can you find out which materials will dissolve in water? How will you carry out this test?

▲ How will you know whether the material has dissolved or not?

MATERIALS

Mixing materials with water, see page 80

Soluble or insoluble?

Name _____ Date _____

Code letter of material	Description of material	What happened when the material was mixed with water?	Was it soluble or insoluble?	Name of the material

▲ Which materials did not dissolve in water?

▲ Which materials dissolved in water?

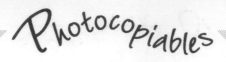

Dissolving a material in water

Name _____   Date _____

What do we want to find out?

How are we going to carry out our test?

How will we know when the material is no longer dissolving?

What we will need to measure:

What we will need to keep the same each time:

MATERIALS

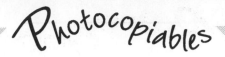

Making a saturated solution, see page 84

Saturated solutions

Name _____   Date _____

Amount of material we added each time	How many stirs before the material dissolved	Observations and comments

The total amount of soluble material we used was _____

▲ Were any other group's results similar to yours?

▲ What is a saturated solution?

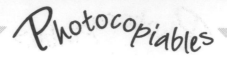

Assessment – Classifying materials

1

▲ Write down the names of the materials from which these items are made.

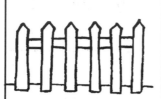

_____ _____ _____ _____

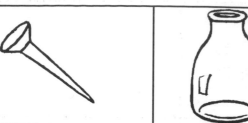
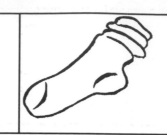
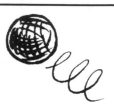

_____ _____ _____ _____

2

These words describe some properties of materials.

hard   strong   breakable   transparent   flexible

▲ Choose two of the words which best describe these items.

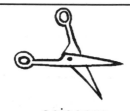

| piece of rock | metal spring | glass vase | scissors |

_____ _____ _____ _____

| plank of wood | plastic bag | T-shirt | bicycle tyre |

_____ _____ _____ _____

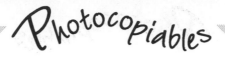

Assessment – Classifying materials

◆ 3

▲ Explain why these materials have been used to make these items.

copper for wire		plastic for hosepipe	
glass for windows		steel for girders	
stone for paving		wood for furniture	
wool for clothing		iron for fridge magnet	

◆ 4

▲ Which of these items is magnetic? Tick the boxes.

scissors ☐	pebble ☐	pencil ☐	paper-clip ☐
aluminium can or foil ☐	nail ☐	washing-up bowl ☐	book ☐

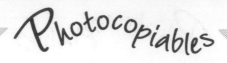

Assessment – Classifying materials

5

Some materials are better thermal insulators than others.

Why is a wooden spoon useful for stirring hot soup?	
Why is a tough plastic handle useful on a saucepan?	
Why do some people put a tea cosy over their teapot?	
How do carpets help to keep a room warm?	

6

Some materials are better at conducting electricity than others.
▲ Tick the materials below which are good electrical conductors.

copper		rubber	
rock		steel	
plastic		glass	
brass		paper	
fabric		wood	

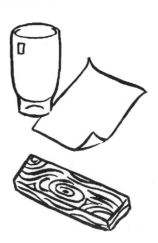

Assessment – Classifying materials

7

▲ Write down the names of three types of rock.
▲ Describe ways in which rocks can be different from each other.

8

▲ Write down the names of two types of soil.
▲ Describe ways in which soils can be different from each other.

MATERIALS

Assessment – Classifying materials

9

▲ Sort these items into solids, liquids or gases.
Write the names in the correct boxes.

dustbin
oxygen
brick
milk
smoke
blood
car exhaust fumes
petrol
sun-hat
glass jar
carbon dioxide
cooking oil

Solids:	Liquids:	Gases:

10

▲ Decide whether these containers are designed for holding solids, liquids or gases. Some containers could be useful for holding more than one of these.

Assessment – Classifying materials

11

▲ Decide if the properties below belong to a solid, a liquid or a gas. Write them in the correct boxes. Some properties might belong to more than one box.

has no shape of its own.	A solid ...
finds its own level.	
is easily held in the hand.	A liquid ...
spreads out in all directions.	
flows easily through a pipe.	
has a definite shape.	A gas ...
can be squashed into a smaller volume.	

12

▲ Find the solids, liquids and gases in each of the pictures below. What are they being used for?

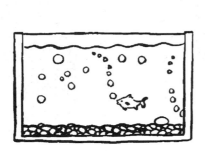

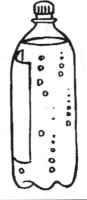

MATERIALS

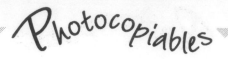

Assessment – Changing materials

1

▲ Describe the changes that happen to the materials during these processes. Are the changes reversible or not reversible?

Process	Material	What happens to the materials	Reversible or not reversible
baking	dough		
freezing	water		
melting	chocolate		
burning	wood		
boiling	water		
mixing	salt and water		
evaporating	water		
burning	wax		
baking	clay		
melting	ice		
mixing	sand and water		
burning	paper		

Assessment – Changing materials

2

▲ What is the usual temperature for the statements on the right?
Draw a line from each statement to the correct point on the thermometer.

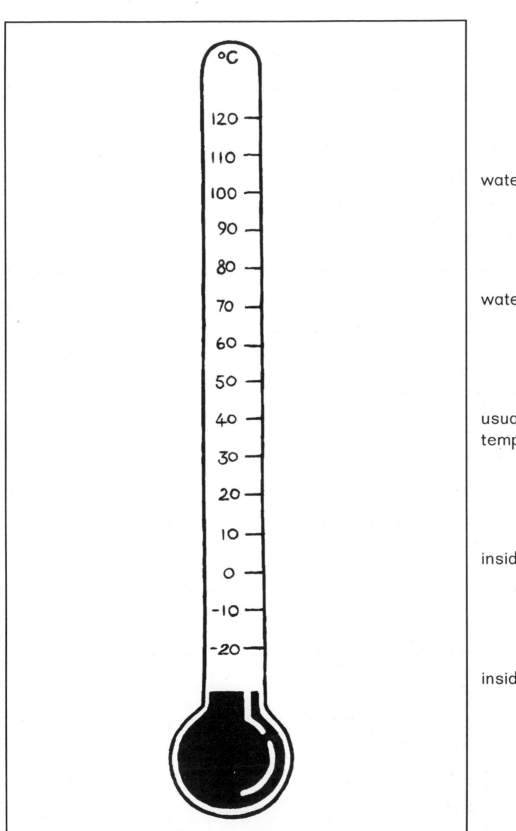

water boils

water freezes

usual classroom
temperature

inside a freezer

inside a refrigerator

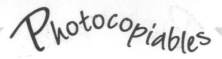

Photocopiables

Assessment – Changing materials

▲ Identify these processes in the kitchen shown below:

dissolving   boiling   melting   condensing   freezing   evaporating

▲ Draw lines to link the words to the parts of the picture they describe.

▲ Describe what is happening to the water in these pictures. What do you think will happen next in each case?

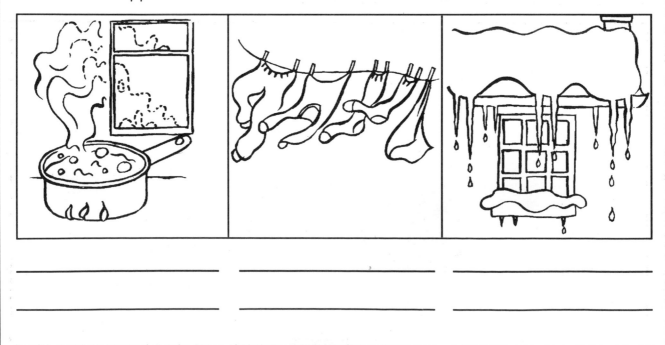

_____   _____   _____

_____   _____   _____

_____   _____   _____

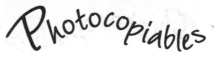
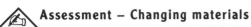
5

▲ Put these sentences into the correct order to describe the water cycle. You can start at whatever point you like. Write the sentences drawn in the space below.

Water vapour rises into the air.

Water drains into rivers.

Water evaporates from the sea.

Rain falls on land.

Rivers flow into the sea.

Clouds are formed.

Cooler air causes condensation.

_____

_____

_____

_____

_____

_____

▲ Draw a diagram to show the water cycle.

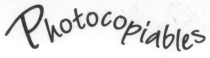

Assessment – Separating mixtures

1

▲ Describe how a mixture of sand and pebbles can be separated.

2

▲ Sort these materials according to whether they are soluble or insoluble in cold water.

bath salts   salt   sand   sugar   chalk   talcum powder   flour

Soluble materials:

Insoluble materials:

3

▲ When you add a material to water, how can you tell if it has dissolved?

MATERIALS

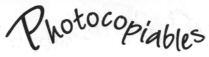

Assessment – Separating mixtures

4

▲ How can muddy water be made clean again?

5

▲ How can salt be separated from water?

6

▲ What is a saturated solution?

INFORMATION TECHNOLOGY WITHIN SCIENCE

The information technology activities outlined in this book can be used to develop and assess children's IT capability as outlined in the National Curriculum. Types of software rather than names of specific programs have been mentioned, to enable teachers to use the ideas regardless of the type of computer they have access to.

The scientific study of materials lends itself to a number of different IT activities. Many of the activities centre around word processing, but there are also several opportunities for data handling and measuring. The activities in this book are very practically based, and give children opportunities to use concrete materials and resources in order to develop scientific understanding. Content-specific software should not be used to replace such experiences, and should be used to develop or reinforce understanding only after initial practical work. Teachers should be aware that although such software may assist pupils in their learning of science, it may add little to the development of their pupils' IT capability.

Using CD-ROMs

A number of the IT activities in this book suggest the use of an encyclopaedia CD-ROM to allow children to search for topic-related information. As CD-ROMs are really huge databases containing text, pictures, sounds and even moving images, their use for this purpose forms part of the information handling aspect of IT capability.

When children first use a CD-ROM, they may be content to 'browse' the disk. Although this helps them to gain an idea of the type of information the disk contains, the way it is structured and how to move around it, children can quickly become overwhelmed by the vast quantity of information, and will need a clear focus if their search is to become purposeful.

One of the most important areas to teach is the way to create a search for specific information. This could be done from a list of keywords, or by entering the topic you are looking for into a search box. The software will then search the entire CD-ROM and let you know how many matches it finds. Children will need to be shown how to move to each successive match and decide whether it is relevant – a task which clearly calls for higher-order reading skills. Some software also allows children to add 'bookmarks', so that they can easily come back to a useful section.

Other CD-ROMs are more interactive, and children will find that by clicking with the mouse on a highlighted word they will be taken automatically to a cross-referenced article, which may or may not have relevance to their search. It is easy to get lost as you hop from one page to another. If children have any experience of using the Internet, they will find this use of a CD-ROM similar to the 'World Wide Web'

pages which create links between computers in different parts of the world.

Once children have located the relevant information, they may want to print it out or save it for use with other software (for example, on a word processor). If text is to be edited or extended, it should be saved as either *plain* or *ascii* text. This creates a file which contains only the characters of the text and excludes any formatting or printing commands. Such files can usually be used on any other computer. The actual procedure for saving text in this way will depend on the CD-ROM and the software.

Other types of CD-ROM provide children with collections of pictures which they can use to illustrate their work. The pictures can be saved on to a disk and then included within word-processed text, or even altered in a graphics package.

Extracting material from a CD-ROM raises the issue of copyright, and teachers should be aware of this. However, it is only likely to become problematic if children are publishing their work outside the school. If in doubt, check with the publishers of the CD-ROM.

Spreadsheets

Spreadsheets are versatile and powerful tools which can be used in a variety of ways in science activities. A spreadsheet is like a large set of ordered and classified pigeon-holes. Any pigeon-hole or *cell* can contain data in the form of text and numbers (and even pictures in some cases), or a formula which uses keyed-in numbers to calculate an answer (which appears in the same cell). The different cells are referenced by a co-ordinate system with letters on the x axis and numbers on the y axis.

All spreadsheets contain a set of predetermined formulae which will, for example, add up the numbers in a set of cells or average a set of data. There are also quick ways of replicating a formula down or across the spreadsheet, so that the cell references are automatically updated as well. The numbers can be formatted to lie within the centre of a cell, on the right or lined up by the decimal point; the widths of the columns can be changed and text styles added to make the results more attractive.

One of the spreadsheet uses suggested in this book is for children to record their investigative science work. The matrix arrangement of the spreadsheet suits many tasks, and is particularly useful where children are collecting a series of results and then finding the average. A formula can be set up to calculate this directly. The spreadsheet can be used in this way for a series of measurements from a single group of children, or for a class record where each row contains the results from a different group of children.

Most spreadsheets also contain simple graphing facilities which enable children to plot one set of data against another. These graphs are easy to set up, and mean that children need only type their data once in order to present it in a range of formats.

IT links

The grids below relate the activities in this book to specific areas of IT and to relevant software resources. Activities are referenced by page number (in bold where activities have expanded IT content) rather than by name. The software listed in the second grid is a selection of programs generally available to primary schools, and is not intended as a recommended list.

AREA OF IT	TYPE OF SOFTWARE	ACTIVITIES (PAGE NOS.)		
		CHAPTER 1	CHAPTER 2	CHAPTER 3
Communicating Information	Word Processor	17, 21, 32, 33, 39, 42, 47, 50	54, 72, **73**, 75	
Communicating Information	Art/Graphics software	21, 30, 37, 50	64, **73**, 75	
Communicating Information	Authoring software	**22**, 25	**73**	
Communicating/ Handling Information	CD-ROM	**22**, 35, 39, 44, 47, 48	**63**, **73**	
Information Handling	Database	**14**		
Information Handling	Branching database	16, 38		
Information Handling	Graphing software	23	**63**	83, **84**
Information Handling	Spreadsheet	23	**63**	**84**
Measurement	Measuring	30	60, 62, **63**	
Control	Control	46		

SOFTWARE TYPE	BBC/MASTER	RISCOS	NIMBUS/186	WINDOWS	MACINTOSH
Word Processor	Pendown Folio	Desk Top Folio Pendown	All Write Write On	Creative Writer Kid Works 2 Creative Writer	Kid Works 2 Easy Works
DTP	Typesetter Front Page Extra	Impression Style Desk Top Folio 1st Page	Caxton Press NewsSpaper	Microsoft Publisher	
Multimedia Authoring		Magpie Genesis Key Author		Genesis MMBox2	Hyperstudio
Database	Datashow Grass Pinpoint Junior	DataSweet Find IT	Grass Sparks Pinpoint Junior	Sparks Claris Works	Claris Works Easy Works
Branching Database	Branch	ReTreeval	Branch		
Graphing Software	Datashow	Pictogram DataSweet	Datagraph	Datagraph Easy Works	Easy Works
Spreadsheet	Grasshopper Pigeonhole	DataSweet Grasshopper Advantage	Grasshopper	Sparks Claris Works Excel Starting Grids	Claris Works
Measurement	Sense-it	ReSound Junior Insight	Investigate	Insight Investigate	

MATERIALS

	ENGLISH	MATHS	HISTORY	GEOGRAPHY	D & T	ART	MUSIC	RE
CLASSIFYING MATERIALS	Speaking, listening and writing: Which is the best material, plastic or wood? Story writing: The life story of a plastic bottle; Adventures in a hot air balloon. Compile crosswords and other word games to include materials and properties. Reading: *The Stone Book* by Alan Garner. Stories about alchemists.	Collect statistics associated with use and waste of materials to make graphs, pie charts. Survey of building materials.	Roman buildings and walls. Anglo-Saxon buildings. Viking boats. Tudor houses and ships. Victorian machinery and transport. Britain since 1930 – new technology, plastics. Ancient Greek pottery, jewellery, buildings. Non-European buildings. Local study – use of materials locally.	Localities – geology, raw materials extracted, materials used; buildings, jobs, environmental problems. Management of waste. Local recycling initiatives. Environmental change – sustainability.	Explore strength in structures; how characteristics of materials relate to their uses. Design and make model boats from wood, plastic, foil, paper, card. Design posters to proclaim the properties and usefulness of wood, plastic, metal; or to discourage waste. Use waste materials where possible.	Draw, sketch or paint still-life collections of materials, machinery, rocks. Make rubbings of wood and metal. Create collages out of wood turnings, waste materials. Make models and sculptures from wood, metal, plastic, newspaper. Make pictures and models of hot air balloons.	Collect, make and demonstrate musical instruments made out of different materials. Compose musical pieces to portray different materials. Create musical pictures to represent solids, liquids, gases.	Explore the use of materials to build places of worship; use of materials in ceremonies. Discuss the responsibility of using the Earth's supply of materials.
CHANGING MATERIALS	Collect word families associated with the processes. For example condense, condensing, condensation; freeze, freezing, frozen. Write poems creating a hot or cold mood. Create a dramatic representation of the water cycle. Compile crosswords and other word games to include the processes and changes.	Collect information about hot and cold temperatures – use the data to draw graphs. Explore minus numbers.	Explore the making of pots and bricks by Romans, Victorians, Greeks and locally.	Discover the hot and cold places of the world. Emphasise local water cycles. Study river systems and water reclamation.	Plan a party – cook pancakes, eggs, potatoes, cakes. Make invitations, menus, chef's hats, table decorations.	Make and bake dough models. Paint a representation of the water cycle. Create collages to represent hot and cold. Create cartoons depicting processes and changes.	Compose music to represent stages in the water cycle. Write a rap or song including processes and changes.	Collect examples of the importance of candles and burning in religious ceremonies.
SEPARATING MIXTURES	Create a glossary to explain the terms: dissolve, solution, soluble, insoluble, mixture, filter, sieve, separate.	Create time trials for separating different-sized particles from a mixture.		Find out about the extraction of salt from mines and from the sea. Discover how water is cleaned, how pollution can be avoided.	Design and make a filtering system to clean water.	Draw detailed sketches of crystals.	Make sounds to represent different-sized particles.	